HAWAIIAN REEFS

A Natural History Guide

by
Ron Russo

Photos & Illustrations
by
Ron Russo
unless otherwise noted

Wavecrest Publications

Published in North America by
WAVECREST PUBLICATIONS
P.O. Box 921
San Leandro, CA 94577-0092
USA

ISBN 0-9635696-0-0

Printed by Lorraine Press
           Salt Lake City, Utah

 *Printed on Recycled Paper*

DEDICATION

I would like to dedicate this work to my three sons: Ron, Jr., Ken, and especially Brian, who accompanied me on countless research trips for other books.

And finally to Reggie Lewis: my uncle, my friend; who was taken from this life prematurely and whose love touched many.

ACKNOWLEDGMENTS

A number of generous people provided technical review and assistance, support, specialized services or encouragement during the research and production of this book. I want to extend my heartfelt appreciation to all for taking time out of their busy schedules to help. This book would have been impossible without them.

I want to thank John E. Randall and Robert H. Cowie (Bishop Museum), Dusty Chivers, Terrence Gosliner, and Gary Smith (California Academy of Sciences), Lucius Eldridge (Pacific Science Association), Ann Fielding (Island Explorations), Loiselte Marsh (Western Australian Museum) Patricia R. Bergquist (University of Auckland), Mary K. Wicksten (Texas A&M University), E. Alison Kay, Isabella Abbott, Celia Smith, Julie Bailey-Brock, Evelyn Cox, Paul Jokiel, Richard Grigg, and Dave Gulko, (University of Hawaii), Gordon Hendler (Natural History Museum of Los Angeles), Dave Pawson (Smithsonian Institution), Jim Maragos (East-West Environment and Policy Institute), Bruce Carlson (Waikiki Aquarium), and finally Alex Kerr (University of Guam) for their technical assistance.

I want to extend a special thanks to Sue and Ed Robinson for their cooperation, quality dive services, and select photographs. I would also like to thank the staffs of Lahaina Divers and Ed Robinson's Diving Adventures for their commitment to safety, enjoyment, conservation, and assistance in locating a number of species. While I resided in a number of hotels, the warm hospitality of the staff of the Kahana Reef Hotel in Maui made my stays pleasurable. Gratitude is also extended to Sandra McCormick of Creative Computer Graphics for the production of the manuscript, the galley, and layouts; to Barbara Downs for her illustrations of the crab gall and gall crabs; and to Pam Frazier for her generous technical advise. A special thanks goes to Linda Pieretti for always being there.

I have made every attempt to incorporate the suggestions of reviewers and taxonomists. Any errors, however, are my sole responsibility and not that of the scientists mentioned.

"Whenever I find myself growing grim about the mouth;
whenever it is a damp, drizzly November in my soul,
then I account it high time to get to sea as soon as I can"

Ishmael
Moby Dick
Herman Melville

CONTENTS

cauliflower coral, *Pocillopora meandrina*

PREFACE

This book is intended for anyone who seeks to explore and better understand the reefs of Hawaii.

This book is by no means a comprehensive work. The marine eco-system around the Hawaiian Islands is so vast and rich, with so many plants and animals that are either not well known, new to science, or not even identified. While some groups are well repre-sented within these pages, others like algae are barely touched. The natural production limitations of a book like this would not allow for complete coverage of all the marine life to be found, which might require a lifetime of work and thousands of species.

Within this book, a number of species appear for the first time in a published work for the general public with their proper scientific names. I have also included a few species whose taxonomy is not as yet clear. The taxonomy of many species and groups is complex and in states of flux. The scientific names provided are based on the best knowledge currently available. Information is consistently provided on physical descriptions, habitat, food, enemies, interest-ing behavior and range.

Much of the work for this book was done around the Islands of Oahu, Maui, Molokini, and Lanai.

I invite you all to use this book and the many other excellent refer-ence guides listed at the end of this book to learn about and enjoy the reefs of Hawaii. They are indeed a treasure.

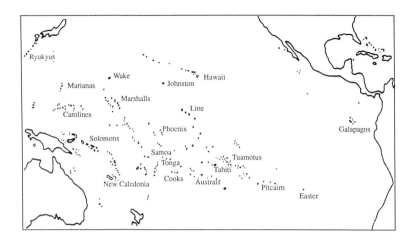

Major island groups of the Central and South Pacific (after Stoddart, 1992)

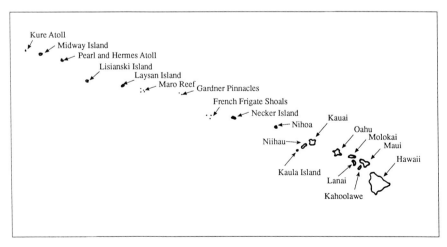

Hawaiian archipelago

HAWAIIAN REEFS

INTRODUCTION

Hawaii sits at the northern edge of the tropical zone in the Pacific. This is the most isolated chain of islands in the world, rising alone in a vast expanse of open ocean. Its nearest neighbors, the Phoenix, Line, and Marshall Islands, lie over a thousand miles away to the south and west. Because of this isolation and the cooler waters surrounding them, the Hawaiian Islands do not have as many marine species as found in Micronesia or elsewhere in the South Pacific.

Hundreds of thousands of years ago, marine species dispersed here, mainly from the Indo-Pacific. Many of these animals found Hawaiian waters to be suitable habitat. From these ancestral parents, many new species evolved that are found no where else in the world. This makes Hawaii a unique marine environment.

Unfortunately, this island paradise is seriously threatened. More Hawaiian terrestrial species have already gone extinct than in all of North America. The future of Hawaii's biological riches lies in the hands of dedicated scientists, wildlife biologists, and concerned and careful users like you.

Main Hawaiian Islands

THE FORMATION OF HAWAII

Most of the Hawaiian Islands are actually underwater. These Islands are merely the tops of massive volcanoes, which lie beneath the sea. More than 85 percent of the islands are submerged. They are the tallest mountains in the world, if measured from the sea floor. Mauna Kea, on the island of Hawaii, is the highest volcano in the Islands rising 4205 meters (13,796 feet) above sea level and over 10 kilometers (6.2 miles) above the sea floor.

THE PACIFIC PLATE

The earth's crust is divided into several plates that sit atop the deeper mantle. The Pacific Plate, from which the Hawaiian Islands rise, is moving north-westward toward the Aleutian Trench at the rate of about 9 centimeters (3.5 inches) a year. The Plate moves over what scientists believe is a permanent **"hot spot"** in the earth's mantle, which has been active for over 70 million years. At this hot spot, molten lava breaks through the cooler Pacific Plate floor forming undersea volcanoes. As these volcanoes repeatedly erupt, they build rising toward the surface, eventually forming islands. As the Plate moves northwest away from the hot spot, the northern-most island volcanoes cool and die. New volcanoes form in succession where the Plate moves over the hot spot, eventually creating a chain of undersea volcanoes and islands. Volcanoes that cool before surfacing or old islands that sink below the surface are called **"seamounts."**

THE HAWAIIAN-EMPORER CHAIN

The Hawaiian-Emporer Chain of islands and seamounts extends over 6000 km (3726 mi) to the northwest. It includes over 100 volcanoes, most of which are seamounts. At the juncture where the northern-most seamounts in this chain drop into the Aleutian Trench, they are assimilated into the earth's hot mantle.

The Hawaiian Islands are slowly sinking back into the sea. Eventually, they will all become seamounts. The rate at which subsidence or sinking is occurring is not alarming. On Oahu, for example, the rate is about 0.3 millimeters (.01 in) per year. At Hilo, Hawaii, the rate is about 2.4 mm (.09 in) per year. Drowned reefs have been discovered near Lanai that now exist at depths where no reef could live, which implies their historic nearness to the surface. Here, coral growth apparently could not keep up with the island's subsidence and the rapid rise in sea level following the melting of continental ice sheets in the post-glacial period.

The oldest of the Hawaiian Islands is the northern-most island of Midway at about 27 million years. Kauai is approximately five million years old. The youngest island, Hawaii, is at the southern end of the chain and is about one million years old. Actually, there is a seamount 28 km (17 mi) south of Hawaii called Lo-ihi that will become the next island in about 10,000 years. This growing volcano is presently within 970 m (3182 ft) of the sea surface. While Lo-ihi sits over the Hawaiian Hot Spot, it will continue to erupt and grow toward the surface.

CORAL REEF FORMATION

What we commonly call **"coral"** is actually the calcareous skeleton of thousands of tiny stinging animals, called **"polyps"** that extract calcium and other minerals from the sea. Coral polyps feed by capturing microscopic prey called **"plankton."** More importantly, reef-building coral animals have dinoflagellate algae, called **"zooxanthellae"**, living within their tissues. Reef-building corals must be in relatively strong sunlit areas, usually less than 30 m (98 ft). The maximum depth at which corals can actively build reefs is about 46 m (150 ft).

In the presence of light and carbon dioxide, zooxanthellae are able to produce a portion of their own food supply through **photosynthesis.** The relationship between coral polyps and these algal partners is still not well understood, but may involve the algae absorbing waste products from the coral animals, while in turn providing organic carbon, oxygen and other compounds to the polyps. Hawaiian corals, deprived of planktonic food organisms, grow quite well in strong light. Experiments have shown that without these algal partners, reef-building corals usually grow poorly and often wither and die.

As reef-building corals grow toward light, older coral below is smothered forming massive limestone foundations. Coral reefs are a mixture of coral animal skeletons, as well as those of echinoderms, crustaceans, mollusks, coralline algae, and sediment.

TYPES OF CORAL REEF:

Coral reefs began forming around the first Hawaiian Islands about 500,000 years ago. While there are several different types of reefs, only a few are found in the Hawaiian Islands. These include: **fringing**, **barrier**, and **atoll reefs**. Other reef types including bank and patch reefs are more predominant elsewhere in the Pacific.

The most dominant and youngest type of reef in the Hawaiian Islands is the fringing reef. The islands of Oahu, Maui, Molokai, and Kauai have extensive fringing reefs. Fringing reefs grow close to shore and typically have a shallow inner lagoon or back reef. These back reefs generally have fewer species than outer reef environments.

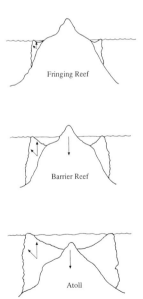

Stages of reef development

Fringing reefs often ring small islands. Along large islands, fringing reefs are usually in linear sections offshore with large gaps between sections, which allows tidal movement and the outward flows of fresh water from rainfall runoff. Occasionally, torrential flood conditions produce large amounts of freshwater runoff that lingers inside a lagoon for too long before mixing with open ocean. Coral animals and other inshore species subjected to lowered salinity for too long a period perish. The recovery of a coral reef community may take decades after a severe storm. The most vulnerable corals, of course, are those closest to shore where sedimentation, wave action, and pollution are more likely.

Atolls develop over a period of thousands of years as the great weight of an island depresses the relatively thin crust of the earth causing the island to slowly sink. If the rate of island sinking is slower than coral growth, corals may ultimately reach the surface forming a crescent or nearly complete ring. Near the surface, coral begins trapping sediment at accelerated rates. As the debris builds up forming beaches, plant seeds delivered by wind, birds, and ocean currents take root in the sand. Although the crest of the reef may be buried under debris, the outer edge of the reef continues growing. Atolls are found in the northwestern, older islands of the Hawaiian chain at Lisianski Island, Hermes Reef, Midway, and Kure.

Barrier Reefs occur where the reef is separated from the shore by a relatively deep, wide lagoon. The reef at Kaneohe Bay, Oahu has the form of a barrier reef, but it isn't a true barrier reef because it hasn't grown seaward from shore, but, instead formed on top of a ridge. A barrier reef developed along the west coast of Kauai when sea levels were lower, but it is now considered a submerged reef.

INSHORE HABITATS:

There are several different types of habitats along island shores where visitors can find interesting plants and animals. These include: reef slopes, coral reef, sand flats, coral rubble, boulder fields, and massive underwater volcanic rock formations. Along the immediate shore, there are sand beaches and volcanic rock outcroppings that support unique plants and animals. Some habitats may be exposed at low tide. Tidal differences in Hawaii vary only about 1 m (3 ft) compared to nearly 12 m (40 ft) in Alaska.

> **REEF SLOPES:** Reef slopes occur on the outside of coral reefs where the surf swell breaks. The plankton-rich water is generally cleaner, less turbulent, and is inhabited by many species of urchins, sea stars, sea cucumbers, and fishes. These slopes support several butterflyfishes, moray eels, and sharks.

> **CORAL REEF:** Healthy coral reefs are a rich mixture of several species of live corals, algae, and a variety of fishes and invertebrates. Coral reefs include deep coral reefs, reef crests, and shallow reef flats, which are different in physical form and composition. Where corals grow within a few feet of the surface, ocean swells break creating an extremely turbulent area. The species that survive here are firmly attached or capable of taking refuge within coral branches and are adapted to strong light and wave surge. The brown algae *Turbinaria ornata* is common in the wave break or reef crest zone.

SAND FLATS: Vast areas of sand exist between patches of coral reef and often extend inshore to form beaches. Sand flats support different kinds of species than reefs, even though reef fishes often cruise over open sand. Sand flats are home to box crabs, sea cucumbers, flatfish, snails, worms, and a variety of other species. Orangeband surgeons, *Acanthurus olivaceous*, and several goatfishes often feed in sand flat areas. Sand is usually created through the combined forces of wave action on dead coral and calcareous algae and the coincidental feeding habits of parrotfishes, who eat algae, but take in bits of coral and later defecate sand particles.

Sand flat off Black Rock at night

CORAL RUBBLE: A lagoon of calmer water usually develops inside a fringing or barrier reef toward shore. Corals broken off and killed by storm action are often found in the lagoon area. While there may be massive heads of live lobe coral, *Porites lobata*, in a lagoon, smaller chunks of dead coral serve as growing sites for a broad variety of algae. Sometimes, vast areas of dead coral occur in deep areas as a result of storm damage. Nudibranchs, rock-boring urchins, crabs, shrimps, and brittle stars are often found in coral rubble areas.

BOULDER: The boulder environment is well suited to any organism that requires a hard substrate to settle on. Algae, coral, sponges, tunicates, sea stars, and rock-boring urchins are common here. Boulder environments are also favorite places to see many of the algae-eating surgeonfishes, particularly convict tangs, *Acanthurus triostegus*. In areas where large boulders are stacked one on another, squirrelfishes hide in the crevices.

VOLCANIC ROCK FORMATIONS: Underwater volcanic rock formations take on the appearance of massive mounds, caves, and lava tubes. These places are a photographer's delight since many species of corals, sea stars, algae, crabs, lobsters, and fishes occur here. The orange cup coral, *Tubastrea coccinea*, and the black coral, *Antipatharia dichotoma*, are usually found in caves. Sea turtles are sometimes found resting on the wave-protected sides of gigantic wash rocks.

SANDY BEACHES: Because of the exposure to the elements, predation, and the shifting nature of sand, sandy beaches do not support many species. Ghost crabs, *Ocypode ceratopthala*, are the most obvious inhabitants with their mounds and entrance holes along the upper sections of beaches. Amphipods, mole crabs, and polychaete worms also live here.

ROCKY SHORELINE: Where old lava flows reached the sea or where volcanic rocks have been used as rip-rap, a unique assemblage of exposure-tolerant marine organisms thrive. Among all the snails, limpets, seaweeds, and other organisms here, two species usually catch your attention. One is the shingled urchin, *Colobocentrotus atratus*, that resembles a purple flying saucer attached to the rocks. The other is the fast-running rock crab, *Grapsus tenuicrustatus*, that scurries among the rocks.

Exploring a rocky shoreline at low tide

CORAL REEF ECOLOGY

Like any other environment, coral reefs have **producers** (algae and plankton), first level **consumers** i.e., plant eaters or filter feeders (surgeonfishes, tunicates), **predators** (trumpetfish, sharks), and **decomposers** (bacteria). Together, all the animals and plants that inhabit a reef environment keep the system functioning. Each depends directly or indirectly on others. A dramatic increase in the population of any one species can have substantial impacts on other species, as well as the entire reef system. As any one species increases in number, its natural predators often follow suit or the population is ultimately controlled by available food, parasites, and diseases.

> **CORAL REEF FOOD CHAIN:** Plankton are captured by hydroids, who are, in turn, eaten by butterflyfishes. These fishes often become prey to larger fishes including sharks. This simple direct line exchange of food energy from plankton ultimately to sharks is called a **"food chain."** Life on coral reefs, however, is far more complex than a food chain suggests and consists of many overlapping and interconnected energy exchanges as well as other complicated associations.

> **CORAL REEF FOOD WEB:** Basically, all organisms on a reef are interconnected. One prey animal may have several predators, as well as parasites. Each predator, in turn, has parasites, and, perhaps, larger enemies. This complex interplay of multiple prey, predators, parasites and other organisms is called a **"food web."** While coral polyps capture microscopic plankton for food, gall crabs, *Trapezia* crabs and some worms use coral for shelter. Butterflyfishes, with their own diverse array of specialized parasites, eat coral polyps. In turn, butterflyfishes are eaten by moray eels or sharks, who also have parasites. This intricate web of relationships creates the living system or community we know as a coral reef.

CLEANING STATIONS: There are a number of coral heads spread throughout a reef where Hawaiian cleaner wrasses, *Labroides phthirophagus*, and cleaner shrimps, *Lysmata amboinesis*, live. Their locations are widely known to fishes in the area. These places are called **"cleaning stations"**, because reef fishes periodically seek the services provided by the shrimps or the wrasses.

It is not uncommon to see several species of fish milling around a single coral head, patiently waiting their turn. When the opportunity develops, a fish seeking this service usually tilts its body downward or sideways at about a 45 degree angle. The wrasse delicately removes and eats the parasites, which includes copepods and isopods.

A cleaning station with barred filefish and a blacklip butterflyfish

REEF DAMAGE: The brittle nature of coral makes some species particularly vulnerable to damage and even death. Branching species including cauliflower coral, *Pocillopora meandrina*, antler coral *P. eydouxi*, and finger coral, *Porites compressa*, and many others are easily damaged by storms, careless boaters, and divers.

Storms that generate strong underwater surge action can tear reefs apart down to a depth of 15-18 m (50-60 ft), with severe storms reaching 30 m (100 ft). Cauliflower and antler corals that tend to stick out from the sides or tops of boulders, volcanic rock formations, or limestone heads are broken off and roll with surge action. Once removed from their attachment points, coral polyps are smothered by sediment and algae. Some beaches are littered with the fragments of coral branches destroyed in this way.

Boaters who simply drop anchor without checking the bottom first or anchor in sand too close to the edge of a coral reef may destroy patches of coral reef with their anchors and the up and down motion of the chains. Anchor damage, while much less common in the Hawaiian Islands, occurs in other reef systems around the world in staggering proportions. Some Hawaiian tour and dive boat operators are sensitive to this problem and select sandy anchorage spots.

Finally, careless divers who fail to adjust their buoyancy, who drag their gauges, who crash into the bottom with their fins and tanks, and who handle delicate species, cause subtle, but accumulative damage.

While we can't prevent storm damage, a little care in exploring underwater Hawaii can preserve coral reefs for marine species and other people to enjoy. Please familiarize yourself with the guidelines for good "**Coral Reef Etiquette**" provided on page 155 to help conserve Hawaiian reefs.

ALGAE BIOLOGY

GENERAL: Hawaiian reefs and rock formations support a complex diversity of marine algae (limu or seaweed). A few of the more obvious ones are included in this work. Seaweeds are found from the high-tide splash zone to the deepest parts of the reef at the limit of adequate light penetration. Seaweeds play important ecological roles on the reef serving as food, shelter, attachment sites, and providers of oxygen to marine animals. **DESIGN:** Generally, algae are classified based on dominant pigments into four main groups: green (Chlorophyta), blue-green (Cyanophyta), brown (Phaeophyta), and red algae (Rhodophyta). Through photosynthesis algae produces some of their own food (carbohydrates) while releasing oxygen. Seaweeds attach to the bottom by sticky, root-like tissues (holdfasts) or hair-like rhizoids. Some forms are erect, while others are thin, encrusting, calcareous sheets. **REPRODUCTION:** Algae reproduce by either spores (asexual) or gametes (sexual).

GREEN ALGAE

Dictyosphaeria cavernosa

Sometimes called "green bubble algae", this alga is recognized by the large round cells bound together in single-wall fashion creating hollow spheres when young and cups when broken. This alga often forms solid mats 10 cm (4 in) thick from shallow reef flats to deeper areas. This species occurs in the South Pacific and the Caribbean.

Halimeda discoidea

These dark-green clusters of calcified segments are found on old coral heads or emerging out of sandy bottom. This species is able to "root" itself deeply in sand through its sediment-filled rhizoid. Plant clusters reach 7.6 cm (3 in) across. The individual segments are 1 cm (.35 in) or more wide. Finely ground segments of *Halimeda* contribute significant amounts of sand to some Hawaiian beaches. This species occurs in the South Pacific, Gulf of California and the Caribbean.

algae, *Dictyosphaeria cavernosa*

algae, *Halimeda discoidea*

Ulva fasciata

Resembling "see through" lettuce, this green alga has thin, flat, usually twisted, blades up to 10 cm (4 in) wide and often 50 cm (20 in) or more long. This species is common in rocky shoreline tidepools, rip-rap, and headwalls. This species occurs in the Indo-Pacific and Caribbean.

BROWN ALGAE

Dictyota sandvicensis

This species of *Dictyota* flexes with each shift in the current on reef flats and in tidepools. Its yellowish-green iridescence and Y-branched, often twisted blades that measure 3 mm (.13 in) wide and lack midribs, are primary features of this species. Blades sometimes have small side branches. This seaweed reaches about 12 cm (5 in) high. This species occurs south to Easter Island and east to Central America.

Turbinaria ornata

Turbinaria is a stiff, erect brown alga with toothed, rounded turbins and a central stem. It is usually near the outer edge of the reef, but also in tidepools. It reaches 20-25 cm (8-10 in) high. Other algae and hydroids grow on the stems and blades. This species occurs in the Philippines, Samoa, Polynesia and Vietnam.

RED ALGAE

Ahnfeltiopsis concinna

This red alga occupies the high intertidal zone along basaltic rocky shores. Those most exposed are yellowish-green, while plants lower down are dark red. It forms extensive, dense, bushy mats of rubbery, cylindrical branches that reach 18 cm (7 in) high. Many snails and crustaceans are found among its branches. This species occurs in Japan and the Cape Verde Islands, but is likely elsewhere.

algae, *Ulva fasciata*

algae, *Dictyota sandvicensis*

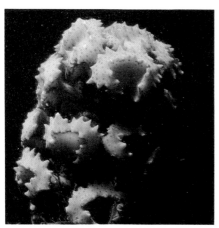

algae, *Turbinaria ornata*

algae, *Ahnfeltiopsis concinna*

Asparagopsis taxiformis

This delicate, fluffy red alga appears in pink, red, and bluish-violet shades. It is usually found along rocky shores, on reef flats, and deep coral reefs where there are strong currents. It occurs in clusters of several erect stalks, reaching 15 cm (6 in) high. This species occurs at Easter Island, Eniwetok, the Philippines and Gulf of California.

Hydrolithon reinboldii

This species is bluish-violet to deep lavender with a knobby surface. It occurs as a calcareous crust on old coral heads or as fist-sized nodules. Nodules are created after algal spores settle on sand particles and reef rubble, growing over and encrusting whatever they settle on. Growth continues as the nodules are rolled about in the surge. This species occurs in the South Pacific and Central America.

Liagora valada

Liagora is a complex genus with its species difficult to recognize without expert help. Yet, members of the genus are common components of Hawaiian reefs. These algae are generally found in the spring, spending the rest of the year in the form of an obscure alternate generation. Spring plants appear as small, round, compact bushes with dichotomous, calcified branches. Color varies in gray, pink, or white shades. Plants are often slimy. This species is found on reef flats and near reef crests. It reaches about 10 cm (4 in) across and high. This species occurs in the Red Sea, Philippines and Central America.

Mesophyllum mesomorphum

This species forms thin, brittle, over-lapping, rose petal-like plates in concentric patterns. Patches of *Mesophyllum* are usually found intertidally under shaded ledges, in caves and holes or in deeper parts of the reef. Patches may exceed 30 cm (12 in).

algae, *Asparagopsis taxiformis*

algae, *Hydrolithon reinboldii*

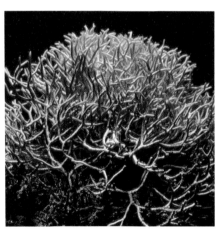

algae, *Liagora valada*

algae, *Mesophyllum mesomorphum*

Porolithon gardineri

This lavender-purple, coral-like, calcareous alga is found across reef flats, usually in areas of strong currents or crashing waves. The tips of the branches may be cyclindrical or fused into flattened fans. Clusters of branches may reach 30 cm (12 in) across. This species occurs in Eniwetok and Easter Island.

Porolithon onkodes

This encrusting calcareous species is typical of high intertidal areas near reef crests and along rocky shores. Sheets of this alga may exceed 51 cm (20 in) across. Limpets, nerite snails, and shingled urchins are usually found on this alga. This is an important species as it helps provide an actively growing reef crest that buffers wave action, allowing other species to exist shoreward. This species occurs in Polynesia, the Philippines, Easter Island and Central America.

SPONGES

A sponge's form is created through the interlacing of tiny fibers and/or **spicules.** Sponges are simple animals that strain water for microscopic plankton and oxygen. Water enters through tiny holes and emerges through larger holes. Sponges possess male and female organs. Tiny larvae pass into open seawater through the large holes. Many sponges have disagreeable odors which may serve as a defense. Snails, sea stars, nudibranchs, and some fishes eat sponges.

Spirastrella coccinea

This brilliant red encrusting sponge is generally found under ledges, on cave ceilings, or other shaded rock surfaces below 15 m (50 ft) or in the open below 30m (100 ft). These sponges occur in small patches or solid sheets that exceed 51 cm (20 in) across. *Berthellina citrina*, a side-gilled sea slug, eats this sponge among others.

algae, *Porolithon gardineri*

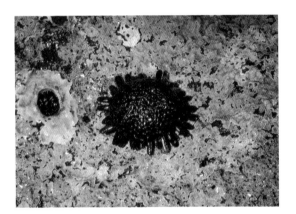

algae, *Porolithon onkodes*

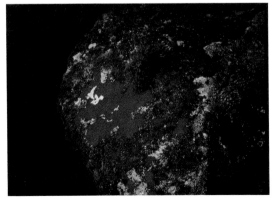

sponge, *Spirastrella coccinea*

29

Dysidea sp.

This orange species forms thick masses with radiating lines running from white-tipped peaks. These sponges occur in deeper parts of the reef, sometimes, mixed with red sponges. They measure from 5-10 cm (2-4 in) across and are round or oblong.

Clathrina sp.

This bright yellow-green calcareous sponge is often found in the open by itself. It forms small clumps rather than solid sheets. Unlike the red sponge, this species occurs rather sparingly across large rock walls. It reaches 8 cm (3 in) across.

CORAL BIOLOGY

GENERAL: There are over 150 species of coral in the Hawaiian Islands. About 40 species are reef builders. Hawaii tends to have fewer species than other island chains in the South Pacific. **DESIGN:** Corals are relatively simple marine animals that resemble anemones, but instead have hard, exterior, calcium skeletons. Coral animals, called **"polyps"**, are usually cylindrical with one or more rings of tentacles armed with batteries of stinging cells surrounding their mouths. There are several types of corals including: **branching, foliaceous** or **plate-like, encrusting, disc-shaped,** and **massive.** More robust forms tend to develop where there is strong surge, while more delicate species occur in sheltered areas. **BEHAVIOR:** The tissues of all reef building corals contain beneficial unicellular algae called **zooxanthellae**, which adds color to the polyp's bodies. Coral growth is strongly influenced by temperature, salinity, nutrient availability, exposure to light and air, the presence of zooxanthellae, and predation by fishes and invertebrates. As a potential adaptation against desiccation, corals exposed at low tide often produce large amounts of mucus. Sometimes, the

sponge, *Dysidea sp.*

sponge, *Clathrina sp.*

mucus combines to form "ropes", which accumulate along the shoreline. Mucus ropes are eaten by other reef animals and may play an important role in reef dynamics. **FEEDING**: Corals feed on tiny zooplankton. **REPRODUCTION:** In some species, reproduction is influenced by the lunar phase and the onset of darkness. Larvae are either produced within the body cavities of adults and expelled into open water, or develop in open water after eggs and sperm are released and the eggs are fertilized. They drift for several hours or months before they settle on hard surfaces and transform.

cauliflower or rose coral, *Pocillopora meandrina*

Commonly found in shallow areas where there are strong currents or wave action, cauliflower coral is an important pioneering coral and is one of the first to colonize new lava flows. A colony is often found by itself on the top or side of a massive lava boulder or rock wall. Its multi-branched form offers shelter to a variety of crabs and fishes. At night, several *Trapezia* crabs are often found on a single coral head among the branches. During the day, they hide. Arc-eye hawkfish are regularly seen resting on top of the branches. Cauliflower coral reaches 40 cm (16 in) or more in diameter. This species occurs in the Indo-Pacific.

antler coral, *Pocillopora eydouxi*

The large, open branches of this coral are usually divided into paired lobes. It occurs in water deeper than 6 m (20 ft). The entire colony can exceed 60 cm (24 in) in diameter. Like other compact, branched corals, antler coral is important as a refuge to many animals, particularly to Hawaiian dascyllus fishes and red *Trapezia* crabs. This species occurs throughout the Indo-Pacific.

coral, *Pocillopora damicornis*

This species occurs within protected bays, the inner portions of reef flats, and other areas where there is little movement of sand and unattached seaweed across the bottom. Some researchers regard this species as an early colonizer of reef flats. It appears to need strong light, since it is typically found in shallow areas above 10 m (33 ft). Clumps of this finely-branched, delicate coral rarely exceed 15 cm (6 in) across. The tips of the branches frequently swell into fan-shaped, hollow enclosures induced by the gall crab, *Hapalocarcinus marsupialis*. These tiny mottled gray and white crabs spend their lives inside the coral gall chambers, feeding on coral tissues and mucus. Some colonies of coral have several of these galls close together. This species occurs from the Red Sea to Panama.

cauliflower or rose coral,
Pocillopora meandrina

compact form,
P. damicornis
(B. Downs)

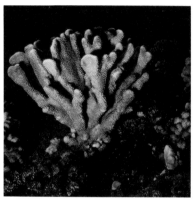

antler coral, *Pocillopora eydouxi*

coral, *Pocillopora damicornis*
(photo by Ed Robinson)

coral gall (B. Downs)

gall crab (B. Downs)

33

lobe coral, *Porites lobata*

Lobe coral is the most common and the largest reef build-ing species in the Islands. Its yellowish-light green color and massive lobed form distinguish it from other corals. Some forms are brown. It is found as an encrusting form or as a large coral head up to 2 m (6 ft) or more across. It occurs inside shallow lagoons where strong wave action develops, but may be as deep as 15 m (50 ft). Snapping shrimps, *Alpheus deuteropus*, sometimes create long, sinu-ous, interconnected brown troughs in the surface of the coral. Tiny hydroids, *Rhizogeton sp.*, usually grow in these troughs and serve as food for some butterflyfishes. This species occurs in the Indo-Pacific.

finger coral, *Porites compressa*

Finger coral is the second most common coral in the Is-lands. Finger coral prefers calm water on the lee sides of islands, wave protected bays, and deep reef slopes. In calm areas, it grows fairly rapidly, sometimes crowding out other corals and forming extensive beds as on the east side of Lanai, where it covers acres. The tall, finger-like colonies can reach 20-25 cm (8-10 in) in height. This coral is para-sitized by the trematode worm *Plagioporus sp.*, which can reduce coral growth by 50 percent. The worm may also spend a part of its life cycle in coral-eating butterflyfishes. This species occurs in Hawaii, Samoa, other tropical ar-eas, but not at the Line or Phoenix Islands.

coral, *Montipora capitata (formerly M. verrucosa in Hawaii)*

This brownish coral with white edges assumes many forms beyond the bracket or plate shape seen here. In this form, the brackets usually overlap. The surface is normally rough with countless rice kernel-like tubercles. It occurs from shallow areas to about 42 m (140 ft). Plates may exceed 51 cm (20 in). This coral is fragile and should be viewed from a distance.

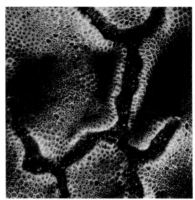

lobe coral, *Porites lobata*   **snapping shrimp channels**

finger coral, *Porites compressa*

coral, *Montipora capitata*   *M. capitata*
plate form   encrusting-knobby form

coral, *Montipora patula*

This encrusting species is easy to overlook. Colonies are usually found growing in between other corals on lava formations or over old coral heads. Like other *Montipora* corals, this species has a rice kernel-like texture over its surface. Its color is tan, fawn-brown, sometimes with tiny bright blue polyps. It grows below 3 m (10 ft). Colonies may exceed 2 m (6.5 ft). Brackets often reach 50 cm (20 in).

blue coral, *Montipora flabellata*

This unmistakable encrusting species is usually seen in shallow water where there is heavy wave action or strong currents. It is bright blue or lavender/purple. Patches often reach 50 cm (20 in) or more across. Apparently, the same snapping shrimp that creates brown troughs in *Porites lobata* attacks this coral. Honolua Bay, Maui has a particularly rich display of this colorful coral.

coral, *Pavona varians*

This fawn-brown, encrusting coral is characterized by its wavy, wrinkled ridges. It is common from near the surface down to about 24 m (80 ft). It is often found at the base of finger coral or encrusting over old coral heads forming sheets that exceed 30 cm (12 in) across. This species occurs from the Red Sea through the Indo-Pacific.

coral, *Montipora patula*   (photo by Jim Maragos)

blue coral, *Montipora flabellata*

coral, *Pavona varians*

coral, *Leptastrea purpurea*

Another easy to ignore but common species, this brown, green, or purple coral forms encrusting sheets on lava or old coral heads in shallow water with heavy wave action. It also occurs in deep reef areas. The ridges that separate individual polyps are angular with no space between polyps. The crab, *Troglocarcinus sp.,* lives in deep pits in this coral. This species occurs from the Red Sea through the Indo-Pacific.

orange tube coral, *Tubastraea coccinea*

The orange tube coral paints the surface of volcanic walls, caves, and ledges, making it difficult to miss. It usually grows above the bottom on rock where currents prevent sediment accumulation, as deep as 30 m (98 ft). It often forms round, clump-like colonies that measure 5-10 cm (2-4 in) across. Since this species lacks the zooxanthellae found in other corals, it depends entirely on its ability to capture minute plankton from passing currents. The difficult-to-find orange nudibranch, *Phestilla melanobranchia*, and the cushion star, *Culcita novaeguineae*, are known to eat this coral. This species occurs worldwide throughout the tropics.

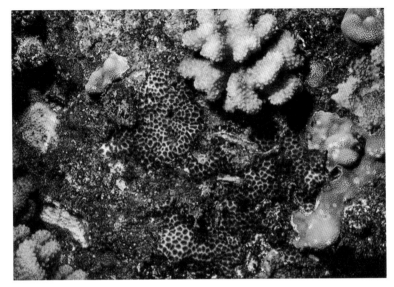

coral, *Leptastrea purpurea*

orange tube coral, *Tubastraea coccinea*

whip/wire coral, *Cirrhipathes anguina*

>The long, flexible sinuous form of this coral distinguishes it from most other Hawaiian corals. It belongs to the black coral family but is a solitary, stiff, yellow-green coral hanging out from walls usually below 15 m (50 ft). It often twists and turns as it grows, sometimes creating weak spirals. It measures about .5 cm (.25 in) in diameter by 1.2 m (4 ft) in length. It captures drifting planktonic animals. Wire coral is host to a tiny commensal goby, *Bryaninops youngei*, and a cryptic shrimp, *Pontonides unciger*. Both of these animals require careful observation to locate. This species occurs in the Red Sea and Indo-Pacific, but its distribution in the Hawaiian Islands appears to be limited to the islands from Kauai south.

black coral, *Antipathes dichotoma*

>In life, black coral appears as a delicate, multi-branched, rusty-orange or white bushy colony. The skeletal branches of dead colonies are black. Colonies are found in 21 m (70 ft) of water in caves and under ledges, but are known to occur over 91 m (300 ft) deep. The fine branches of black coral host large commensal bivalves, *Pteria brunnea,* and other organisms. This species occurs in the Red Sea and Indo-Pacific. In the Hawaiian Islands, it is found from Hawaii to Niihau.

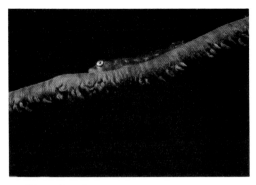

Yonge's goby, *Bryaninops youngei*

whip/wire coral,
Cirrhipathes anguina

wire coral shrimp, *Pontonides unciger*

black coral, *Antipathes dichotoma*

CORAL RELATIVES

hydroid, *Lytocarpus philippinus*

These delicate white, branching hydroids are colonies of tiny animals with oral rings of stinging tentacles. The heads share a common digestive tract and are held together by a chitinous sheath. This species usually occurs in deep reef areas below 14 m (45 ft) on rock surfaces. Their abundance varies as they are considered pioneers in new rock formations. Polyps use their powerful toxins and injection mechanisms to capture plankton. The highly branched colonies often exceed 18 cm (7 in) high. **CAUTION:** Contacting this hydroid with bare skin usually results in a painful rash. This species occurs in the Red Sea and Indo-West Pacific.

green hydroid, *Unidentified*

These short, olive-green, colonial clusters of hydroids are found on deep wall surfaces at a depth of about 14 m (45 ft). Most hydroids reproduce by budding off free-swimming medusae which produce eggs and sperm. Fertilized eggs develop into larvae which ultimately settle onto firm surfaces and transform into polyps. Single polyps grow into feathery colonies by budding off more polyps. This species reaches 8 cm (3 in) high. **CAUTION:** Avoid contact.

snowflake coral, *Telesto riisei*

This delicate, white octocoral grows in deep, dark areas of the reef where currents are strong. It is often found growing in the same areas as black coral down to about 50 m (160 ft). The branches are upright, red or orange at the base, and about 25 cm (10 in) high. The extended polyps are white. This species was first reported in Pearl Harbor, Oahu in 1974. Apparently, it has been introduced into Hawaiian waters. It occurs naturally from Florida to Brazil.

hydroid, *Lytocarpus philippinus*

green hydroid, *Unidentified*

snowflake coral, *Telesto riisei*   (photo by Ed Robinson)

octocoral, *Anthelia edmondsoni*

This soft coral is generally found in bays, harbors, and the leeward sides of islands, particularly Oahu. The small polyps are connected basally by stolons. Tentacles are usually pale lilac to purple, while bodies are tan. Zooxanthellae occur in the tissues of this octocoral. Polyps are 6 mm (.25 in) high when extended. Colonies of 8 cm (3 in) or more coalesce forming broken carpets that often exceed 30 cm (12 in). This octocoral occurs only in Hawaii.

octocoral, *Sinularia sp.*

This true soft coral forms massive colonies that encrust limestone or volcanic rock at depths to 37 m (120 ft) or more. It is particularly evident in several shallower areas around Oahu and southwest Lanai. The soft, flexible texture and the gray (sometimes green or brown) color are distinctive, separating this species from stony corals. A colony may exceed 1 m (3 ft) across. The broad lobes reach 10 cm (4 in) in height. There are two species in Hawaii that are difficult to identify in the field. *Sinularia* is also recorded off Vietnam and Fanning Atoll.

zoanthid, *Palythoa tuberculosa*

These colonial anthozoan soft corals form thick, spongy mats that grow over rock and limestone substrates. When a colony is resting and the tentacles are withdrawn, it resembles a cream-beige sponge or encrusting coral. These zoanthids have much larger tentacles than corals. Colonies are usually 3 cm (1.2 in) or more thick and often exceed 51 cm (20 in) across. Individual polyps measure about 6 mm (.25 in) across. Zoanthids feed on zooplankton. This species occurs throughout the Red Sea and Indo-Pacific.

octocoral, *Anthelia edmondsoni*   (photo by Ed Robinson)

octocoral, *Sinularia sp.*

zoanthid, *Palythoa tuberculosa*

45

polyclad flatworm, *Family Pseudoceridae*

These brilliant fuschia worms with yellow margins and tiny green spots are one of the most striking creatures in Hawaii. This flatworm is found in daylight crawling over limestone and volcanic rocks. Their paper-thin bodies conform to every nuance of rock surfaces as these worms glide seemingly effortlessly forward. Adults reach 3.2 cm (1.3 in) long, and probably eat other worms and small mollusks. This flatworm may occur across the Indo-Pacific.

spaghetti worm, *Loimia medusa*

Long, pearl-white strands stretched out across the sea bottom characterize this well-hidden worm. These spaghetti-sized tentacles radiate outward from a central point where the worm enjoys the protection of its burrow. The tentacles are feeding instruments that collect bits and pieces of detritus and other organic debris. Collected material is transported through cilia-lined grooves in the tentacles to the mouth. Any disturbance causes the worm to quickly retract its tentacles. The tentacles extend 61 cm (24 in) or more from the mouth.

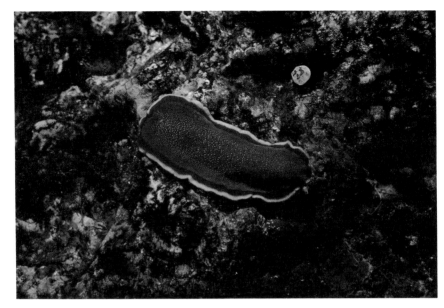

polyclad flatworm, *Family Pseudoceridae*

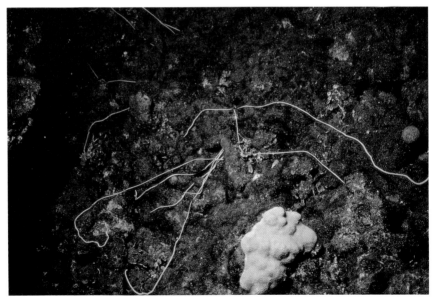

spaghetti worm, *Loimia medusa*

SNAIL BIOLOGY

GENERAL: There are nearly 1000 species of mollusks in the Hawaiian Islands. Of these, an estimated 80 percent are gastropods (snails, sea slugs and related mollusks). **DESIGN**: Some gastropods are recognized by their hard, calcium-carbonate shells. The calcium is extracted from seawater and food and deposited along the edges of shells by the tissues of the mantle. These animals have strong muscular feet, distinct heads, eyes, and sensory tentacles. Some gastropods have a single, horny plate attached to their feet, called an **"operculum"**, which can completely close off access into the shell to protect against desiccation or predators. **FEEDING**: Snails have a tongue-like structure with hard teeth, called a **"radula"**, which in some species are used to scrape algae. Other snails are predatory, using modified radulae as venomous harpoons which inject poisonous compounds into fishes and other mollusks. **REPRODUCTION**: In marine snails, sexes are generally separate and internal fertilization of eggs is common. In other mollusks like sea slugs, each individual possesses male and female organs. In a mating pair, each impregnates the other. Eggs are generally laid on the substrate. The larvae of many species are free-swimming members of the plankton community. Some snails give birth directly to little snails.

nerite, *Nerita picea*

> These round, black snails are found by the hundreds usually crowded together on the sides of rocks, in crevices, or under ledges in the wave-splash zone of rocky shores. Large specimens are about 1.3 cm (.5 in) across. These snails move about often moving away from water to feed on algae. Nerites are drilled and eaten by the snail *Neothais harpa*. Empty shells are used by intertidal hermit crabs. This snail appears to be rare in the Pacific, except at Johnston Island and in Hawaii.

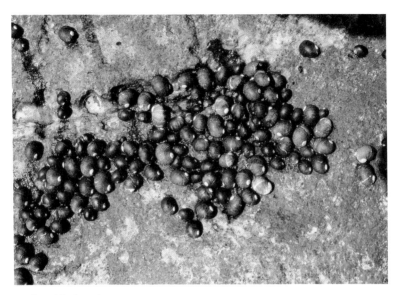

nerite, *Nerita picea*

nerite, *Nerita polita*

    This species is neither as abundant nor as obvious as its cousin *N. picea*. The shell is mottled gray and white. Sometimes the white markings appear flame-like. These snails live in sand under boulders in the intertidal zone. Adults reach 3.4 cm (1.3 in) across. This snail is rarely seen in day, but usually emerges at night when it crawls over rocks grazing on algae. This species occurs throughout the Indo-West Pacific.

periwinkle, *Littorina pintado*

    These are the highest living marine snails in Hawaii. This periwinkle spends much of its time out of water wetted only by occasional wave splash. During the day at low tide, the shell entrance may be closed by the operculum to avoid drying out. It secretes a mucous material that dries out, gluing the snail to the rock. Shells reach 1 cm (.4 in). At high tide, these snails move about feeding on algae. It spawns throughout the year, releasing eggs into the water. Larvae are planktonic. A female may lay 82,000 eggs per year. This snail occurs from the Indo-West Pacific to East Africa.

Serpulorbis, *Serpulorbis variabilis*

    These snails cement their hard, coiled shells against the surface of rocks. This species is usually found along wave-washed shores down to 14 m (46 ft). The white-rose striped shells measure up to 5 cm (2 in) across. This snail lacks an opercula. It captures plankton and drifting detritus with mucous threads that extend out of the shell's entrance. The food laden mucous is later ingested. This species also occurs in the Marshall and Line Islands.

nerite, *Nerita polita*

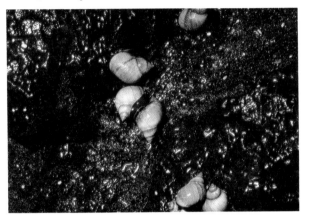

periwinkle, *Littorina pintado*

Serpulorbis, *Serpulorbis variabilis*

limpet, *Cellana exarata*

Known as "opihi" to Hawaiians, these cap-shaped mollusks live below the wave splash zone usually submerged, except at low tide along with periwinkles and nerites. This species clings tightly to rock surfaces and resists the dislodging force of oncoming waves. The dark gray shells have raised, black, radiating ribs from the apex to the margin. Shells reach 4 cm (1.5 in) across by 2 cm (.75 in) high. On hot days when exposed at low tide, these limpets may raise their shells away from the rock allowing air to circulate around the muscular foot. This limpet occurs throughout the Hawaiian Islands.

limpet, *Cellana sandwicensis*

These brown-black limpets are found a bit lower in the intertidal zone, usually on coralline algae where there is continuous splash. Occasionally, the shells appear white due to a calcareous deposit. The prominent ribs usually extend beyond the edge of the shells creating a scalloped appearance. This species creates "**home scars**" where individuals routinely and snugly fit into precise depressions in the rock. Also called "opihi", these limpets spawn in December and January. Shells measure about 4.3 cm (1.6 in) across and often have algae growing on them. This species is found only in the main Hawaiian Islands.

limpet, *Cellana exarata*

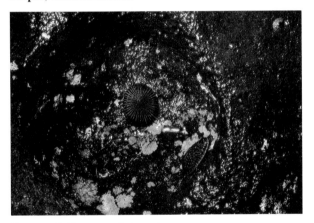

limpet, *Cellana sandwicensis*

Isognomon, *Isognomon perna*

> This shallow-water, under-rock bivalve is common in inches of water at low tide on rocky shorelines. The buff-yellow shells have brown radiating lines. The shell you see is longer than the interior shell, which is attached to the rock by byssal threads. The low profile of these bivalves provides minimal resistance to the rush of water that surges around them with every wave. Shells measure up to 5 cm (2 in) long. These bivalves are filter-feeders, capturing plankton. This species ranges through the Indo-West Pacific to Hawaii.

NUDIBRANCH BIOLOGY

GENERAL: Sea slugs or nudibranchs, which means "naked gills", are among the sea's most beautiful and delicate mollusks. **DESIGN**: Unlike their distant relatives, the land snails and marine snails, sea slugs lack outer protective shells. Instead, sea slugs are often camouflaged by cryptic design. Acid and the borrowed stinging cells of prey are defensive mechanisms for many species. **BEHAVIOR**: Many of Hawaii's nudibranchs lead secretive lives hidden beneath coral rubble or among the sponges, hydroids, or the corals preyed upon. Some emerge only at night. Others are frequently seen out in the open in daylight. **REPRODUCTION**: These mollusks have both ovaries and testes (eggs and sperm). Mating involves two individuals: each one fertilizing the eggs of the other.

Isognomon, *Isognomon perna*

Pteraeolidia ianthina

This flamboyant sea slug crawls about in the open feeding on hydroids where it is unmolested by predators. This sea slug absorbs the hydroid's stinging cells without triggering them. These cells are transported through the branches of the intestine to the tips of the projections, called "**cerata**" that cover their backs. Here, the stinging cells become borrowed defensive weapons. **CAUTION**: These nudibranchs can inflict a mildly painful stinging reaction when touched. This is the second longest nudibranch in Hawaiian waters reaching 10 cm (4 in) or more. This species is widespread throughout Hawaii and the Indo-Pacific.

Phyllidia varicosa

Unlike other "dorid" nudibranchs, the gills of *Phyllidia* are located along the lateral margins of the body. The yellow-tipped knobs, firm bodies, and varying patterns of gray and black are distinguishing characteristics. Adults reach 9 cm (3.5 in), eating sponges that possess a potent toxin. This toxin accumulates and becomes a pungent defense mechanism for this sea slug. This species is common throughout Hawaii and the Indo-West Pacific.

Phyllidia pustulosa

These firm sea slugs have a bold color pattern of pink and black. This species is found in daylight in a variety of habitats, but especially in areas of abundant live coral. This species is sometimes difficult to see among pink corralline algae. Adults reach 2.5 cm (1 in), eating sponges with similar results to *P. varicosa*.

Pteraeolidia ianthina

Phyllidia varicosa

Phyllidia pustulosa

57

Phyllidiella rosans

This small, gaudy sea slug is difficult to miss. It is distinguished by the numerous, longitudinal pink ridges against a black background. The black, chemoreceptive "**rhinophores**" are pink at the base and the foot is gray. It reaches 35 mm (1.4 in) in length. It has been found at depths of 20 m (66 ft) around Oahu, southwest Lanai. It is also known to occur in various island groups of the western Pacific and Indian Oceans.

gold lace nudibranch, *Halgerda terramtuentis*

These gelatinous-like sea slugs are usually seen in daylight in areas where there are sponges and orange cup corals. The opaque white body marked with orange, interconnected, web-like lines distinguishes this species. Adults grow to 3 cm (1.2 in) and feed on sponges. This species may occur throughout the South Pacific.

Spanish dancer, *Hexabranchus sanguineus*

These are among the largest and most striking nudibranchs in the world. Their size and brilliant red or red-orange color distinguishes them. This giant sea slug is usually found at night crawling over rocks. Occasionally, it flares out its mantle into wing-like appendages that undulate from the front to the rear, while it arches its back up and down in a graceful, mid-water ballet. Adults reach 30 cm (12 in) long. This sea slug's red or rose colored, coiled ribbons of eggs are 3.5 cm (1.5 in) across. The eggs and the adult sea slugs possess compounds called "**macrolides**" (regarded as the most potent fish repellents reported). These chemicals are extracted from sponge prey and concentrated more than ten times in the eggs. A bright red, tiny commensal shrimp lives on the back of this giant Indo-Pacific sea slug. Like other invertebrates, these creatures are delicate and vulnerable to human disturbance. **PLEASE, LEAVE THEM WHERE YOU FIND THEM.**

Phyllidiella rosans

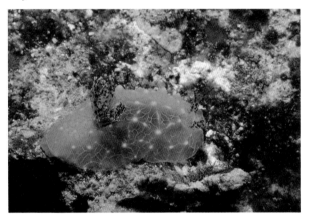

gold lace nudibranch, *Halgerda terramtuentis*

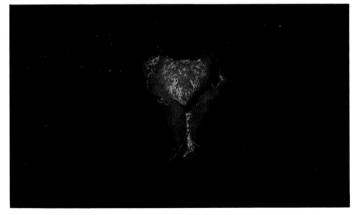

Spanish dancer, *Hexabranchus sanguineus*

MORE MOLLUSKS

sacoglossan, *Plakobranchus ocellatus*
>This common species also has a soft body, but is in a different order than nudibranchs. It is recognized by its yellow-green to light beige color and tiny, ringed spots. These animals blend in with their environment among hydroids and seaweed in coral rubble and silty areas of bays. Adults reach 4 cm (1.6 in). This mollusk spawns year round, depositing eggs on algae. It occurs throughout the Indo-Pacific.

octopus, *Octopus cyanea*
>Octopuses are highly advanced mollusks without shells. When threatened, individuals can rapidly change color from chocolate to mottled white and brown and, then, back to chocolate within seconds. This quick change may startle a predator long enough to allow escape. If an attack is pressed, the octopus may release dark-brown ink that clouds the water and temporarily masks their escape or confuses a predator like a moray. This species is found in holes from shallow inshore areas down to 49 m (160 ft). This octopus is active in daylight. It grows to about 51 cm (20 in) eating crabs, shrimps, and other mollusks. This species occurs in the Indo-West-Pacific.

sacoglossan, *Plakobranchus ocellatus*

octopus, *Octopus cyanea*

CRUSTACEAN BIOLOGY

GENERAL: Crustaceans include such familiar groups as: crabs, shrimps, lobsters, isopods, amphipods, and barnacles. Crustaceans fulfill a variety of roles on the reef including predators, prey, grazers, and scavengers. Some even act as "**cleaners**" removing parasites from other animals. **DESIGN**: Crustaceans have hardened outer skeletons made of chitin (a natural plastic) impregnated with calcium carbonate. In some cases, the thin skeletons are collapsible, and easily damaged. With barnacles, the outer shell plates are hard, thick and are retained throughout life. The skeleton of a crab is shed each time the animal's growing flesh exceeds its capacity. Soft, expandable, new skin forms underneath the carapace. Crabs inflate new, wrinkled skins to their full size by taking in water. Their activity level is reduced until the new skin hardens. **BE-HAVIOR**: Claws are used for grooming, defense, gathering, tearing, and delivering food to their mouths. **REPRODUCTION**: Fertilized eggs are usually held under the abdominal plates in crabs or under the tails in shrimps and lobsters. The larvae become free swimming components of the zooplankton community.

banded coral shrimp, *Stenopus hispidus*

These small red and white shrimps are usually found in crevices and under ledges from shallow inshore areas to deep reefs alone or in pairs. Their long, white antennae usually draw attention to their presence. Adults grow to about 5 cm (2 in). In some parts of their range, these shrimps act as "**cleaners**", removing parasites from fishes. It is not yet known whether these shrimps perform this service in Hawaii. This species is found throughout the Red Sea and Indo-Pacific.

banded coral shrimp, *Stenopus hispidus*

fountain shrimp, *Stenopus pyrsonotus*

These nearly all white shrimps with pink or orange-flushed faces, single red dorsal stripes, and long white antennae are found alone or in pairs below 14 m (45 ft). It occurs in crevices and under ledges. Females carry powder blue egg masses under their tails in July. Adults grow to about 10 cm (4 in) with antennae more than twice as long. These shrimps may provide a cleaning service to fish. This species is also found in New Caledonia and Mauritius, but its range is likely much broader.

carid shrimp, *Brachycarpus biunguiculatus*

These small shrimps are found under coral rubble and rocks during the day. Color ranges from bright red, mottled brown to greenish. The long pinchers are characteristic for this species. Adults reach 5 cm (2 in). There are some reports of this shrimp providing a cleaning service to fishes in some parts of its range. But in Hawaii, this shrimp doesn't appear to enjoy the same immunity as other "**cleaners**", which suggests it does not perform a cleaning function here. Saddle and yellowtail coris wrasses make quick meals of these shrimps when exposed. This species appears to have a world-wide tropical distribution.

spiny lobster, *Panulirus marginatus*

Lobsters hide by day in caves, large crevices, and under ledges. At night, they prowl across the reef in search of food, but ever wary of morays. Spiny lobsters do not have claws like their distant relatives from Maine. When disturbed, their powerful tails quickly propel them backwards. Adults reach 41 cm (16 in). Lobsters are scavengers feeding on a variety of organic material.

fountain shrimp, *Stenopus pyrsonotus*

carid shrimp, *Brachycarpus biunguiculatus*

spiny lobster, *Panulirus marginatus*

hairy hermit crab, *Aniculus maximus*

This large hermit crab is distinguished by its bristly yellow legs and size. Often, the only parts of this crab showing are the eyes, antennae, and hairy legs protruding from the shell it has claimed for refuge. The legs of this species are 10 cm (4 in) or more. Their soft stomach is usually shaped like a spiraled coil that snugly fits into the deepest areas of the shells, anchoring the animals to the borrowed shelters. This species usually uses the shells of large snails like the partridge tun, *Tonna perdix*, or the triton's trumpet, *Charonia tritonis*.

anemone hermit crab, *Dardanus cf. pedunculatus*

This unique hermit crab is distinguished by its large size and the presence of anemones, *Calliactis polypus*, on the back of its borrowed snail shell. The two are symbiotic and are always found together in Hawaiian waters. The anemone's feeding opportunities are increased because of the mobility of the crab. The hermit crab, in turn, gains protection from some predators, since the slightest disturbance causes the anemones to close and expel long threads called "**acontia**", that are laden with toxic stinging cells (see photo). The hermit crab transfers the anemones from shell to shell as it seeks a new or larger shelter. In Hawaiian waters, these animals are found down to 40 m (131 ft). The hermit crab normally forages at night and is found elsewhere in the Indo-Pacific. The anemone has a slightly broader range occurring on other hermit crabs from Japan to western Central America, as well as the Indo-Pacific.

hairy hermit crab, *Aniculus maximus*

anemone hermit crab, *Dardanus cf. pedunculatus*

box crab, *Calappa cf. gallus*

This crab appears to be a form of *C. gallus*. The beige, lumpy carapace of these crabs makes them look more like rocks than crabs. This crab is found under rocks, sometimes intertidally. The claws are held close to the face. The edge of the carapace, which reaches 6.4 cm (2.5 in) across, extends over the legs concealing them, reducing the chances of predation by fish. The claws are used to crush small snails on which it feeds. This species occurs in the Indo-Pacific, Red Sea, and tropical Atlantic.

rock crab, *Grapsus tenuicrustatus*

These rocky shoreline crabs live in the wave-splash zone and are extremely fast. When approached, these crabs run and jump from rock to rock, retreat deep into tight crevices, or jump into the water, where they rarely stay for long. Their colors help camouflage them. The flat body design allows them to fit into crevices and withstand the force of wave-wash without being dislodged. These crabs use the pointed tips of their legs to grip the rock when climbing or facing an oncoming wave. The carapace of large specimens reaches 8 cm (3 in) across. This species occurs in the Red Sea and Indo-Pacific.

crab, *Percnon planissimum*

These extremely fast subtidal crabs are found in shallow, inshore, sandy areas where there are scattered boulders or coral rubble for shelter. This species occurs under the same rocks with swimming crabs. It is recognized by the lime-green line down the center of the carapace, the tiny, bulbous claws, and the spines along the front edges of the legs. The flat carapace reaches 4 cm (1.6 in) across. This species occurs in the Red Sea and Indo-Pacific.

xanthid crab, *Etisus splendidus*

These large red-orange crabs are frequently seen at night among subtidal rocks and boulders. Their legs are prominently spiny and hairy. The claws have spoon-shaped tips. The carapace reaches 18 cm (7 in) across. This species occurs in the Indo-Pacific.

box crab, *Calappa cf. gallus*

rock crab, *Grapsus tenuicrustatus*

crab, *Percnon planissimum*

xanthid crab, *Etisus splendidus*

swimming crab, *Thalamitoides cf. quadrideus*
This species appears close to *T. quadrideus*. Other authors have referred to this crab as *Thalamita integra*. Swimming crabs have a broad, flat paddle-like fifth pair of legs. These crabs are found in shallow intertidal areas with sand bottom and scattered boulders. Swimming crabs are extremely fast. Their color helps camouflage them against the sand. The carapace reaches 6.3 cm (2.5 in) across. This species eats small fishes and invertebrates. This species occurs in the Red Sea and Indo-Pacific.

ghost crab, *Ocypode ceratopthala*
Ghost crabs decorate Hawaii's sandy beaches with their cone-shaped piles of sand and small burrow entrances. By day, ghost crabs generally remain out of sight, although young crabs frequently scurry from open ground to their burrows in a blur of movement. Adults emerge at night. These crabs are extremely fast and have many escape tactics. If prevented from re-entering their burrow, for example, ghost crabs may run into the surf, returning with the next wave as it washes up the beach. Little time is spent in the water because of predaceous fish. If further disturbed, these crabs often dig into the sand and stay there until its safe to return to their holes. Males build large, fan-shaped mounds of sand .6-1 m (2-3 ft) away from their burrow entrances. Mounds may rise 25 cm (10 in) above the level of the beach. Burrow entrances range from 1.5-5 cm (.5-2 in) across. Ghost crabs constantly work their burrows, removing excavated sand and tossing it away from the tops of their mounds. Ghost crabs are scavengers and predators. Adult crabs measure 5 cm (2 in) across the carapace. Mature males have stalked eyes with long, pointed tips. This species occurs in the Indo-Pacific and along the east coast of Africa.

swimming crab, *Thalamitoides cf. quadrideus*

ghost crab, *Ocypode ceratopthala*

Maui beach with ghost crab mounds

71

BRYOZOANS

Bryozoans are colonies of tiny animals that filter plankton from the water. Some bryozoans appear plant-like, while others form encrusting, single-layer sheets on seaweed, shells, and rocks. Some Hawaiian species are prominent even though most are little known.

lace bryozoan, *Reteporellina denticulata*
> These delicate bryozoans are extremely brittle so **PLEASE** avoid touching them. This bryozoan appears to thrive in deeper parts of the reef below 21 m (70 ft) and is quite abundant at 33.5 m (110 ft) in some areas. These bryozoans are usually found on the sides or tops of volcanic rocks or old coral heads where currents deliver plankton and minimize the danger of being suffocated by sediment. Clusters of branches reach about 8 cm (3 in) across by 5 cm (2 in) high.

ECHINODERMS

Sea stars, sea cucumbers, and urchins belong to a group called **echinoderms**, which means "spiny-skinned". These animals are characterized by having an internal, pressurized, water vascular system which operates tube feet with tiny suction discs at the tips. Fluid pressure in the body cavity maintains their body form. Tube feet are used for respiration, locomotion, gripping the substrate, and in some cases, passing food to the mouth. Urchins and sea stars also possess small pincers that are used to kill the larval forms of species, like barnacles or sponges, that might otherwise settle on their backs and clog their respiratory organs. Echinoderm bodies are generally divided into five radial parts.

lace bryozoan, *Reteporellina denticulata*

GENERAL: Hawaiian sea urchins are found from the highest splash zone to the abyssal deep. There are at least eight notable species here. **DESIGN:** Urchins have fragile, thin-shelled, spherical bodies armed with spines. The shells of most species are 5-15 cm (2-6 in) across. The shells, called **"tests"**, are made of calcium carbonate extracted from seawater. Spines are connected to the tests in a "ball and socket" fashion. Muscle fibers encircle these ball and socket joints and control the movement of the spines. Spines can be tilted or waived in the direction of a predator. **FEEDING**: Urchins primarily eat algae, but, they will consume animal flesh. The mouth is centered on the underside and is made of five calcareous plates shaped like an old lantern, referred to as **"Aristotle's Lantern."** **REPRODUCTION**: Sexes are separate. Eggs and sperm are released into open water where eggs are fertilized. Larval development may take several months before transforming into adults. **ENEMIES**: Large snails, sea stars, and fish (particularly wrasses) are primary predators.

slate pencil sea urchin, *Heterocentrotus mammillatus*

These are Hawaii's most widely known urchins. This species usually occurs on deep reefs and are often wedged into crevices of volcanic rock or coral heads. Occasionally, these urchins are in the open in numbers. The thick, blunt, triangular, solid, red or maroon colored spines make this urchin unmistakable. These spines reach 7-12 cm (3-5 in) long. In between these spines are short, flat, plate-like, white, pink, or red spines, which protect the soft tube feet and pincers underneath. Bodies measure about 7 cm (3 in). **AVOID** disturbing them for use as photo props. This species occurs in the Red Sea and Indo-West Pacific.

slate pencil sea urchin, *Heterocentrotus mammillatus*

pebble collector urchin, *Tripneustes qratilla*

Pebble collectors occur throughout the shallow subtidal zone of a reef. These urchins are often found on the tops or sides of coral heads in exposed situations where you rarely find other urchins. Their name comes from their habit of using their tube feet to grip shell fragments, algae, coral, detritus and other loose pieces. With this collection of "reef junk" and the short 2 cm (.8 in) spines, they are not as noticeable as other urchins and may gain some protection from predators as a result. Adults grow to about 15 cm (6 in) across. This species occurs in the Red Sea and Indo-Pacific, north to Japan.

sea urchin, *Diadema paucispinum*

These black-bodied urchins bear the longest spines of any Hawaiian species, which easily reach 20 cm (8 in) or more. The shorter, secondary spines do not have barbs. These spines are brittle and break off easily, which can cause secondary infections embedded in the flesh of fish or people. **DO NOT ATTEMPT TO HANDLE THIS URCHIN**. These urchins are usually found in deep reef areas, often clustered in groups in coral or rock crevices. Divers need to be careful they don't accidentally brush contact these urchins as they descend. Bodies measure about 15 cm (6 in) across. This species also occurs in the Gilbert Islands.

sea urchin, *Echinothrix calamaris*

These urchins occur in deep reef areas, more often alone than in large groups. The black and white banded spines range from 10-15 cm (4-6 in). Banding is common among young animals and may persist into maturity. At night, some slant their spines towards central points forming separate, compact clusters. Bodies reach 13 cm (5 in) across. The shorter, secondary spines are barbed and poison-tipped. They can cause necrosis and cysts if left embedded in your flesh. **DO NOT HANDLE.** This species can be confused with *E. diadema,* particularly in the young stages. It occurs through the Indo-Pacific, north to Japan.

pebble collector urchin,
Tripneustes qratilla

sea urchin, *Diadema paucispinum*
(photo by Ed Robinson)

sea urchin, *Echinothrix calamaris*

sea urchin, *Echinothrix diadema*

As adults, these urchins usually have a blue-green iridescent sheen to the spines. When young, the spines are banded
black and white. These spines are shorter than in *D.
paucispinum*, reaching 10-15 cm (4-6 in). The secondary
spines are poison-tipped. **DO NOT HANDLE.** This urchin occurs either in the open or in rock and coral crevices. In spite of their well-armored appearance, predacious
fishes manage to get through the defensive spines on oc-
casion. This species occurs in the Indo-West Pacific, north
to Japan.

rock boring urchin, *Echinometra mathaei*

These urchins are found in large colonies inshore, in shallow rock and coral reef areas. Normally, this species is
found burrowed into old coral heads or in live coral. Occasionally, individuals are found under coral rubble, rocks,
and ledges, but are rarely exposed. The spines are pink-
beige and measure about 4 cm (1.5 in). The oval bodies
reach about 5 cm (2 in). Rock boring urchins burrow into
the substrate through the combined action of rubbing
spines, scraping mouths, and the pull of tube feet. Once
inside a burrow, these urchins never leave. This species
depends exclusively on organic matter, particularly algae,
falling into the pits. Trapped material is transported by the
tube feet to their mouths. Once these urchins die, their pits
are used by other marine species for refuge and attachment. The related forms of this complex species occur in
the Red Sea, Indo-West Pacific and north to Japan.

sea urchin, *Echinothrix diadema*

rock boring urchin, *Echinometra mathaei*

shingle urchin, *Colobocentrotus atratus*

These dark purple urchins live only on rocky, wave-washed shores where individuals are exposed to the full force of incoming waves. This species is the only Hawaiian urchin found out of the water. Some spines have been reduced to short, lateral projections measuring 1.6 cm (.63 in). The spines over the back are plate-like, fitting together like roof tiles, which helps shed water from oncoming waves and prevents desiccation of the soft tissues beneath. Their low profile helps reduce the danger of being dislodged by waves. Adults reach 6.4 cm (2.5 in) across. The snail, *Vexilla vexillum*, eats this urchin. This species occurs in the Indo-West Pacific.

sea urchin, *Eucidaris metularia*

These small urchins are usually found alone under coral rubble from shallow, inshore areas to deeper parts of reefs. This urchin is rarely in the open. The spineless apical area is characteristic for this species. The short, thick, blunt spines may function only to wedge them in place, since there are so few of them. Once exposed, these urchins are easy prey to hungry wrasses, particularly the yellowtail coris. Both the body and the spines measure about 2.5 cm (1 in) each. Commensal slipper snails are often found on the spines. Other species of *Eucidaris* may occur in Hawaii. This species occurs from East Africa through the Indo-Pacific, north to Japan.

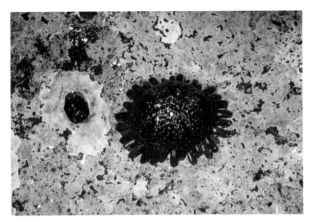

shingle urchin, *Colobocentrotus atratus*

sea urchin, *Eucidaris metularia*

SEA STAR BIOLOGY

GENERAL: There are relatively few Hawaiian sea stars compared to the cooler mainland North Pacific, where along Vancouver Island alone, there are over 70 species or the East Indies with 89 species. **DESIGN:** Sea stars have a central disc as a body with radiating arms. Sea stars range in size from about 2 cm (.75 in) to 1 m (39 in). Typically, there are five arms, but some species have as many as 40. Sea stars can move in any direction with the help of tube feet found in ambulacral grooves radiating from the central mouth on the underside. The dorsal surface of sea stars is usually covered with spines, tubercles, ridges, plates, and tiny pincers. **FEEDING:** Sea stars eat encrusting sponges, ascideans, snails, oysters, barnacles, worms, bryozoans, other sea stars, urchins, coral, and dead fish. Some have restricted diets. Some evert their stomachs to cover their prey, digesting them outside of their bodies. When attacking an oyster, an everted stomach can enter the oyster through an opening in the shell as small as 0.1 mm (.004 in). **REPRODUCTION:** Some species reproduce by dividing the disc into halves, with each regenerating the missing half. A few cast off single arms, which regenerate new discs and corresponding arms. The majority, however, release eggs and sperm into the open sea where the larvae develop.

sea star, *Linckia multifora*

These small, thin, five-armed stars generally occur in subtidal, deep-reef areas on lava and limestone formations. Color patterns vary with combinations of pink and red mottling with blue-gray arm tips. The skin has a smooth, minutely pitted appearance. Adults reach 15 cm (6 in) across. These stars pinch off arms to reproduce. Recently detached arms are often found crawling about without any sign of regeneration. A single, arm with four stubby arms protruding is called a "**Comet Star.**" This species occurs in the Red Sea and Indo-West Pacific.

sea star, *Linckia multifora* (adult)

sea star, *Linckia multifora* (reproductive arm with buds)

sea star, *Linckia multifora* (separated reproductive arm)

sea star, *Linckia guildingii*

These olive green, granular-skinned stars are usually found in deep reef areas among coral heads and rock formations and, occasionally, in shallow water. Adults measure 30 cm (12 in) or more across. Often, their long, cylindrical, sinuous arms are wedged so tightly into crevices or holes that it is difficult to see the whole animal. **PLEASE AVOID** injuring this star by trying to remove it. Enjoy them where found. This species occurs in the Caribbean and the Indo-Pacific.

cushion star, *Culcita novaeguineae*

These large, rounded, cushion-like stars are covered with short spines or tubercles. Cushion stars are usually mottled in shades of red, gray, and orange. These sea stars live in deep reef areas. While distinct arms are absent, a close look at their underside reveals the normal ambulacral grooves of a sea star. Adults reach 25 cm (10 in) across, eating algae, sponges, corals, and detritus. A tiny commensal crab lives in the ambulacral grooves on the underside. This species occurs in the Indo-Pacific, north to Japan.

crown-of-thorns sea star, *Acanthaster planci*

These well publicized giants have been known to decimate entire sections of coral reefs in parts of the tropical Pacific. A large population may include 15 or more individuals in .9 sq. m (10 sq ft). This species usually occurs in deep reef areas alone or in numbers. Bodies are covered with inch-long venomous spines that cause painful wounds. **DO NOT ATTEMPT TO HANDLE.** Adults grow to about 40 cm (16 in) across with 12 or more arms, although some specimens have been recorded at 70 cm (28 in). The triton's trumpet snail, *Charonia tritonis*, and the harlequin shrimp, *Hymenocera picta*, eat this sea star among others. This species occurs in the Indo-Pacific.

sea star, *Linckia guildingii*

cushion star, *Culcita novaeguineae*

crown-of-thorns sea star, *Acanthaster planci*

brittle star, *Ophiocoma pica*

These chocolate brown, fast-moving stars are usually found beneath coral rubble and boulders and in coral crevices during the day. Unlike sea stars, who are in a separate class, the arms of brittle stars are distinct from the body, are highly flexible, and easily break off. The tube feet of brittle stars lack suction discs. At night, they emerge to stretch their arms up into passing currents to capture tiny, drifting animals and other organic material. This brittle star grows to 13 cm (5 in) across. Wrasses are daytime predators. This species occurs in the Indo-Pacific, north to Japan.

SEA CUCUMBER BIOLOGY

GENERAL: Sea cucumbers are sluggish, sausage-shaped creatures that appear motionless on the bottom. Worldwide, there are over 900 species. Hawaii has several notable species. **DESIGN:** The smallest sea cucumber is just over 2.5 cm (1 in), while the largest is about 1 meter (39 in). Some sea cucumbers have tube feet on their bottom. **FEEDING:** Unlike sea stars and urchins, sea cucumbers have their mouths at one end and their anus at the other. Sea cucumbers have a ring of mucus-covered tentacles around their mouths that constantly trap sand, detritus, mud, or drifting organic material. Later, this nutritious slime enters the digestive tract where organic particles are digested. **REPRODUCTION:** Some species reproduce by brooding their eggs on their undersides or backs. Other species release their embryos to finish development in open water. **BEHAVIOR:** Their work is slow and they may appear vulnerable, but some sea cucumbers have the ability to disgorge internal, spaghetti-like organs, called **Cuvierian tubules,** from their anus that discourages predators and causes a mild rash on exposed skin. These organs are regenerated later. Sea cucumbers host commensal **"pearlfish"**, who live inside their body cavities during the day. At night, the fish exits through the anus to forage. Before daybreak, the fish forces its way back in.

brittle star, *Ophiocoma pica*
(photo by Ed Robinson)

sea cucumber, *Actinopyga mauritiana*

These white-speckled, brown sea cucumbers are usually found inshore where currents are strong. They cling tenaciously to coral heads or rubble. Their grip is particularly strong compared to other sea cucumbers. The dimpled, hard body of this sea cucumber reaches 20 cm (8 in) in length. It has five white teeth or plates around the anus. These sea cucumbers do not readily expel their internal organs. This species occurs in the Indo-Pacific, north to Japan.

sea cucumber, *Actinopyga obesa*

These firm, light-brown to yellow-brown sea cucumbers are usually found in deeper, calmer water than *A. mauritiana* in coral rubble or sandy areas. This species has small tubercles and shallow creases over the body. The anus is surrounded by five yellow teeth. Adults reach about 30 cm (12 in). This species occasionally expels its Cuvierian tubules. It is found from the Philippines, north to China.

sea cucumber, *Holothuria nobilis*

These large, black, firm sea cucumbers are usually found in sandy areas or coral rubble and are often covered with a thin layer of fine sand. The young are often found among volcanic rocks or old coral heads. The wide body is generally smooth, with three or four projections along each side that give it the name **"teat fish"**. Adults grow to 30 cm (12 in) long, and occur from the Indo-Pacific, north to Japan.

sea cucumber, *Holothuria atra*

These black sea cucumbers are slender, somewhat soft, and more common in many areas than its relative *H. nobilis*. This species is found in deep, sandy or coral rubble areas, often with a thin layer of fine sand covering their bodies. Adults grow to 40 cm (16 in) or more. This species usually does not expel its Cuvierian tubules in defense. It is parasitized by *Eulimid* snails. This species occurs from East Africa to Hawaii and Japan.

sea cucumber, *Actinopyga mauritiana*

sea cucumber, *Actinopyga obesa*

sea cucumber, *Holothuria nobilis*

sea cucumber, *Holothuria atra*

sea cucumber, *Holothuria hilla*

These soft giants are usually found among rocks or coral rubble. The body is brown with long, beige projections. This species does not have the rigid form of other sea cucumbers and is quite supple. It is one of the longest sea cucumbers in Hawaiian waters, easily exceeding 51 cm (20 in). This species occurs in the Indo-west Pacific, north to Japan.

sea cucumber, *Bohadschia sp.*

These large brown sea cucumbers have black tubercles over their bodies. This species occurs on sand bottom, but is rarely covered by sand particles. Adults reach 51 cm (20 in) long by 13 cm (5 in) across. They frequently expel their Cuvierian tubules. **CAUTION:** These tubules can cause a mild stinging sensation, a rash on bare skin, get tangled in equipment, and are difficult to remove. It's best to leave these sea cucumbers alone.

sea cucumber, *Stichopus horrens*[1]

These relatively firm sea cucumbers occur around coral rubble, old coral heads, boulder and rock formations. The warty projections are .6-1.3 cm (.25 -.5 in) long. Adults reach 35.5 cm (14 in) long by 7.6 cm (3 in) across. This species occurs from Indonesia, northern Australia, north to Hawaii and Japan.

sea cucumber, *Stichopus chloronotus*[1]

These relatively firm sea cucumbers occur among coral rubble, boulders, and rock formations. The olive-green color is uniform. The body projections are about .6-1.3 cm (.25-.5 in) long. These animals reach 23 cm (9 in) long by 5 cm (2 in) across. This species occurs in the Indo-West Pacific, north to Japan.

[1] The taxonomy of several groups of sea cucumbers is complex and in need of revision, especially *Stichopus*.

sea cucumber, *Holothuria hilla*
(photo by Ed Robinson)

sea cucumber, *Bohadschia sp.*

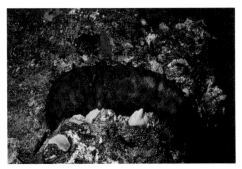

sea cucumber, *Stichopus horrens*

sea cucumber, *Stichopus chloronotus*

TUNICATES

Tunicates are unique in that they are morphologically somewhere between vertebrates and invertebrates. As adults, they appear like many other invertebrates. But, in their larval stage, each possesses a "**notochord**", which is a primitive version of a spinal column. Tunicates occur as either single animals, called "**sea squirts**" or as colonial clusters. Colonies have small intake holes through which plankton/oxygen-rich water is drawn in and filtered. Large holes are collectively used for filtered-water discharge.

tunicate, *Family Styelidae*
> These colonial tunicates form large sheets that cover rock surfaces, particularly in deep reef areas below 18.3 m (60 ft). At first, colonies appear mint green, but with artificial light their beige color is visible. Colonies may measure 25.4 cm (10 in) or more across. Colonies are usually 1.5 cm (.5 in) thick.

tunicate, *(Unknown species)*
> These small colonial tunicates rarely exceed 6.4 cm (2.5 in) across. These tunicates are found below 12 m (40 ft) on rock surfaces among sponges and bryozoans.

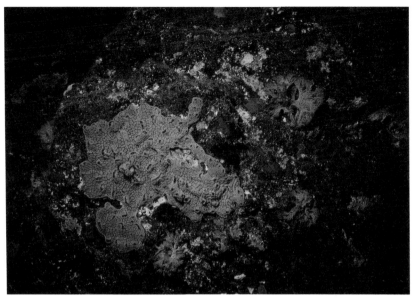

tunicate (unidentified species), *Family Styelidae*

tunicate, (Unidentified species)

FISH BIOLOGY

GENERAL: The waters surrounding the Hawaiian Islands support about 680 species of fishes including those from deep abyssal, offshore pelagic, and reef environments. Just over 400 species are considered reef fishes. **DESIGN**: Most of the fishes covered in this book have bony skeletons. Sharks have cartilaginous skeletons. Skin is an important organ that helps regulate oxygen exchange, excretion, and water pressure. Skin is protected by slime and, in most species, hard overlapping scales. Fins are supported by soft cartilage or by hard, spiny rays. Fins are used as rudders, propellers, stabilizers, brakes, and anti-roll devices to maintain orientation. **REPRODUCTION**: Some fishes reproduce through internal fertilization of eggs and subsequent live birth. Some lay fertilized eggs that hatch outside of the parent. Others deposit eggs on the substrate to be fertilized and guarded by the males. Still others broadcast eggs and sperm into open water where larvae develop and drift for a time near the surface. Reef fishes are among Hawaii's most interesting wildlife. Much can be learned by simply watching their behavior.

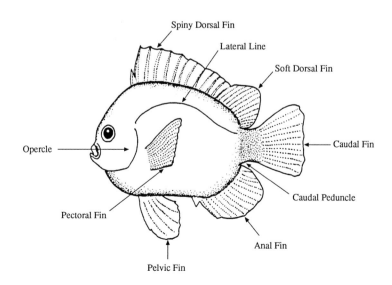

whitetip reef shark, *Triaenodon obesus*

The white tips of the first dorsal and the upper lobe of the tail fin are characteristic of this species, as are the dark blotches on the sides. Whitetips are found resting by day alone or in small groups in caves and under ledges. There is strong evidence that suggests that these sharks have "**home caves**" to which they return routinely after nightly forays. When disturbed, a whitetip slowly cruises over the reef bottom, rarely straying far from it. It has been caught on long-line gear at a depth of 330 m (1082 ft). Whitetips grow to 2 m (6 ft). Prey includes fish, crabs, lobsters, octopuses. Some daytime feeding occurs. While whitetips are occasionally found in the southern islands, these sharks are much more abundant in the Northwest Hawaiian Islands. Whitetips are found throughout the Indo-Pacific from the Red Sea and east coast of Africa to Panama. Although regarded as a docile species compared to other sharks, whitetips have been provoked into aggressive behavior.

whitetip reef shark, *Triaenodon obesus*

orangemouth lizardfish, *Saurida flamma*

Lizardfish have snake-like heads with many sharp teeth showing. The body of this species has indistinct orange-brown bars along the sides and a mottled orange mouth. Lizardfish are usually found sitting on sandy bottom, sometimes partially buried, or on top of coral. This species grows to 30 cm (12 in) or more. Lizardfish eat small fish, which are caught off the bottom. There are nine species of lizardfishes known from Hawaiian waters.

mustache conger, *Conger cinereus*

Congers are related to morays, but are in their own family. Congers stay hidden by day and emerge at night to prowl the reef for food. There are two species in Hawaii. The dorsal fin of this species starts (on a vertical plane) near the front portion of the pectoral fin. This species gets its name from the dark line just under the eye and parallel to the lip. It grows to 114 cm (45 in), eating fishes and crustaceans. It is found throughout the Indo-Pacific.

orangemouth lizardfish, *Saurida flamma*

mustache conger, *Conger cinereus*

MORAY EELS

Morays have been long known for their impressive teeth and their supple, sinuous forms. There are more than 35 species inhabiting Hawaiian waters. Morays are actually much more abundant in Hawaii's coral reefs than diver observations would indicate because they spend so much of their time hidden in the crevices of coral heads or in lava tubes. Morays are rarely completely out of their lair in daylight. More often, divers find an eel with just its head sticking out of a hole. At night, some species wander freely over the reef searching for food. Their fearsome reputation is a bit overdrawn. Morays are capable of inflicting painful bites, but usually only in response to being provoked or threatened. It's best to keep your fingers away from their mouths even though they may appear accustomed to divers.

dragon moray, *Enchelycore pardalis*

> The rarely seen dragon moray, also called the "**leopard eel**", is one of Hawaii's and, perhaps, the world's most beautiful eels with its erect nose tubes and intricate color pattern. Dragon morays have a mouth full of fine, sharp teeth. Some resist leaving their holes even with the temptations that divers offer. This species grows to about 92 cm (36 in). Dragon morays occur from Hawaii and Japan south to Polynesia.

tiger moray, *Uropterygius tigrinus*

> This species is distinguished by the large, irregular, dark round spots against a light beige background. Like other eels, tiger morays share coral heads with other fishes, who maintain a respectful distance. Tiger morays reach 122 cm (48 in). This species is found from Hawaii south through the entire tropical Pacific and Indian Ocean.

dragon moray, *Enchelycore pardalis*

tiger moray, *Uropterygius tigrinus*

snowflake eel, *Echidna nebulosa*

> The snowflake eel is a relatively small, slender eel with distinctive markings. This species is basically white with large black blotches and tiny yellow and black spots. The front of the head is usually solid white. Snowflake eels are found in shallow areas composed of rocky bottom, coral rubble, or on reef flats. This species reaches 71 cm (28 in) and feeds on small crabs and fish. It occurs throughout the Indo-Pacific.

whitemouth moray, *Gymnothorax meleagris*

> These are among the most abundant morays on Hawaiian reefs. This species is distinguished by the all-white mouth, dark yellow-brown to brown body with countless dark-edged white spots. Whitemouth morays grow to 107 cm (42 in), eating swimming crabs, octopuses, and fishes. This species occurs throughout the tropical Indo-Pacific.

undulated moray, *Gymnothorax undulatus*

> The pattern of interconnected pale interspaces and the yellowish cast to the head characterizes this common species. At night, it wanders over the reef searching for food. It grows to 107 cm (42 in), eating crabs, octopuses, and fishes. The moray pictured here ate a large swimming crab within seconds after this photo was taken at night. This species is found throughout the Indo-Pacific.

zebra moray, *Gymnomuraena zebra*

> The striking chocolate background with light yellow bars quickly identifies this species. It may be found in coral heads or cave crevices, sometimes with other morays. Zebra morays grow to 1.5 m (5 ft). Their molariform/cobblestone pavement-like teeth are used to crush the shells of crabs and lobsters. It occurs in the Indo-Pacific and eastern Pacific.

snowflake eel, *Echidna nebulosa*

whitemouth moray, *Gymnothorax meleagris*

undulated moray, *Gymnothorax undulatus*

zebra moray, *Gymnomuraena zebra*

OTHER FISHES

many-whiskered brotula, *Brotula multibarbata*

Rarely seen in daylight, these secretive fish emerge at night to hunt among coral heads and rocks. It occurs from inshore areas to deeper parts of the reef. The large upward-pointing eyes and white chin and barbels distinguish this species. Individuals are usually 46 cm (18 in) or less. Brotulas eat small crustaceans and fishes. This species is found from the Indo-Pacific to east Africa.

trumpetfish, *Aulostomus chinensis*

Trumpetfish occur in light gray-brown, orange-brown, or solid yellow patterns. Like seahorses and pipefish, trumpetfish have long, tubular, elastic snouts. The transparent fins are located close to their tails, which may reduce the chances of any movement alarming prey. Trumpetfish often swim close to the bodies of parrotfish, which may help conceal them from small fish who are unwary of grazing fish. Trumpetfish also take advantage of aggregations of feeding convict tangs, who may disturb small fish. Trumpetfish are also found closely orienting themselves at angles matching geographic features, which likely disguises their presence. Trumpetfish hunt by moving to within striking distance, then lunging forward with a lateral expansion of their snouts, creating a suction that vacuums fishes out of the water. Individuals are found from inshore areas to at least 113 m (370 ft). This species grows to 69 cm (27 in). It occurs from the islands of the eastern Pacific to the Indo-Pacific, but is absent in the Red Sea.

many-whiskered brotula, *Brotula multibarbata*

trumpetfish, *Aulostomus chinensis*

Commerson's frogfish, *Antennarius commersonii*

This species occurs in shades and patterns of beige, yellow, red, brown, black or combinations. It can be easily missed as their motionless, well-camouflaged form blends in with rocks and coral. The limb-like, pectoral fins with elbow joints are used to wedge themselves into rock crevices or against coral. Frogfish do not swim across the reef like other fishes. Instead, individuals wait in place wiggling their first dorsal spine, which may mimic natural food items, to entice small fish to come within striking distance. This fish grows to 31 cm (12 in). It occurs throughout the Indo-Pacific and east to Panama. There are nine species of frogfishes in Hawaii.

SQUIRRELFISHES

Squirrelfishes are elongate, large-eyed, mostly red fish that seek the shelter of caves, boulder piles, and dark ledges by day. At night, squirrelfishes emerge to hunt. Squirrelfishes eat mainly crustaceans. Often, several species occupy the same shelter along with trumpetfish, Potter's angelfish, and whitetip reef sharks. The local Japanese name for these fish is "**menpachi**". There are 16 species in Hawaii.

shoulderbar soldierfish, *Myripristis kuntee*

This species is distinguished by a dark, reddish-brown bar that runs from the top of the gill opening to the base of the pectoral fin and the white first rays of the anal and pelvic fins. When the mouth is closed, the lower jaw extends slightly beyond the upper. It grows to 18 cm (7 in). This species occurs throughout the Indo-Pacific.

Commerson's frogfish, *Antennarius commersonii*

shoulderbar soldierfish, *Myripristis kuntee*

bigscale soldierfish, *Myripristis berndti*

Individual scales of this species are much more noticeable than the preceding species. Also, the dark opercular membrane, creating what appears to be a color bar, extends just below the opercular spine. When their mouths are closed, the lower jaws extend noticeably beyond the upper. This is Hawaii's most abundant squirrelfish from 15-46 m (50 to 150 ft) deep or more. This species grows to 28 cm (11 in). It occurs from the tropical eastern Pacific to East Africa.

crown squirrelfish, *Sargocentron diadema*

The red stripes on these medium-sized squirrelfish are more than twice as broad as the white stripes. The spiny dorsal rays, which are dark red to nearly black in some, have a white band near the base. This species usually occurs offshore. It grows to 16.5 cm (6.5 in). It is found throughout the Indo-Pacific.

Hawaiian squirrelfish, *Sargocentron xantherythrum*

These small squirrelfishes lack white bands near the base of the spiny rays of the dorsal fin. These squirrelfish are usually found close together with many of their kind under large coral heads and ledges. This species occurs in shallow water, but is most abundant at 18 m (60 ft) in many areas. It grows to 16.5 cm (6.5 in) and is found only in the Hawaiian Islands.

bigscale soldierfish, *Myripristis berndti*

crown squirrelfish, *Sargocentron diadema*

Hawaiian squirrelfish, *Sargocentron xantherythrum*

devil scorpionfish, *Scorpaenopsis diabolus*

A well-camouflaged fish, the devil scorpionfish is frequently found in shallow inshore areas among rocks or coral rubble. It is generally found alone resting in crevices, under ledges, or at the base of coral heads. It does not wander over the reef, but instead waits patiently for food to approach. Scorpionfishes are veritable masters of deception. When alarmed, this species moves its pectoral fins forward, exposing a bright orange-yellow area. This is the only humpacked species in Hawaii. This species grows to 31 cm (12 in), eating crustaceans and fishes. It is found throughout the Indo-Pacific. **CAUTION**: Many species of scorpionfishes have venomous spines. **DO NOT** attempt to handle.

Hawaiian turkeyfish, *Pterois sphex*

These graceful, ornate turkeyfish are reclusive, hiding under shelves and in cave crevices during the day. At night, turkeyfish emerge to hunt. The membranes of the pectoral and dorsal fins are deeply incised. It is found from 3-122 m (10-400 ft). It grows to at least 20 cm (8 in), eating mostly crustaceans. While the spines of this species are not as toxic as other members of the genus, it can inflict a painful sting. **DO NOT DISTURB**. This species occurs only in the Hawaiian Islands.

devil scorpionfish, *Scorpaenopsis diabolus*

Hawaiian turkeyfish, *Pterois sphex*

iridescent cardinalfish, *Apogon kallopterus*

Cardinalfish get their name from the red color of many species. This species, however, gets its specific name from the iridescent blue-green color of its scales. These are the most common cardinalfishes in many areas of Hawaii. These fish are nocturnal. During the day, individuals hide in caves or deep crevices in the reef. Males incubate fertilized eggs in their mouths. This species grows to 15 cm (6 in), eating zooplankton. It is found throughout the Indo-Pacific. There are nine species of cardinalfishes in Hawaii.

bandfin cardinalfish, *Apogon taeniopterus*

The white-edged dark bands on the front of the first dorsal fin and the base of the anal and second dorsal fins are distinctive features. Their behavior is similar to the iridescent cardinalfish. This species grows to 18 cm (7 in), eating zooplankton. These cardinalfish are common in Hawaii and have been found in Mauritius, Tahiti, Pitcairn, and the Marshall Islands.

iridescent cardinalfish, *Apogon kallopterus*

bandfin cardinalfish, *Apogon taeniopterus*

HAWKFISHES

There are six species of hawkfishes in the Hawaiian area. All use their thick pectoral fins to wedge themselves among coral branches or into rock crevices to maintain their position and keep an eye on potential food and enemies.

arc-eye hawkfish, *Paracirrhites arcatus*
> This species is distinguished by the "U" shaped arc of orange, with black and light blue edging over each eye. Arc-eyes have two color phases - olive and rose. It occurs from shallow, inshore areas to 305 m (1000 ft). When moving, it goes from coral head to coral head and does not cruise over the bottom. This species grows to 14 cm (5.5 in), eating crabs, shrimps, small fishes, and fish eggs. It is found in the Indo-Pacific.

blackside hawkfish, *Paracirrhites forsteri*
> The dark red spots on the head and the black lateral bar distinguish this species. These are curious fish that will investigate any sign of feeding by other fishes. Their behavior is similar to arc-eyes. This fish also stays close to the bottom. It reaches 22 cm (9 in), eating shrimps and small fishes. Blackside hawkfishes occur throughout the Indo-Pacific.

stocky hawkfish, *Cirrhitus pinnulatus*
> This spotted hawkfish lives in the near-shore surge zone and where there are strong currents. It reaches 28 cm (11 in), eating crabs, shrimps, urchins, brittle stars, and fishes. It occurs throughout the Indo-Pacific.

arc-eye hawkfish, *Paracirrhites arcatus*

blackside hawkfish, *Paracirrhites forsteri*

stocky hawkfish, *Cirrhitus pinnulatus*

redbar hawkfish, *Cirrhitops fasciatus*

The broad, red, vertical bars, black spot on the operculum, and the absence of a bold black spot just beneath the rear of the dorsal fin distinguish this species from the twospot hawkfish. It may reach 13 cm (5 in), eating zooplankton, worms, crabs, shrimps, and small fishes. Their distribution is spotty occurring in Hawaii, Japan, Madagascar, and Mauritius.

OTHER FISHES

bluestripe snapper, *Lutjanus kasmira*

This beautiful fish was introduced to the Hawaiian Islands for commercial harvest from Moorea, French Polynesia in 1956. This species has increased so quickly that it is now abundant throughout the islands and threatens some native species. It occurs in small groups or large aggregations from shallow, inshore areas down to 182 m (600 ft). It usually grows to 25.4 cm (10 in). It is nocturnal, eating crabs, shrimps, and small fishes.

blacktail snapper, *Lutjanus fulvus*

This species was introduced to the Hawaiian Islands from the Society Islands in 1956, where it is the most common snapper. Unlike its relative, blacktails are not yet as common here. In Hawaii, it is usually found alone under ledges or in caves mixed in with soldierfishes or in the open cruising over the reef. It grows to 33 cm (13 in), eating crabs and small fishes. It is found in the Indo-Pacific.

lowfin chub, *Kyphosus vaigiensis*

The large size and silver-gray color with bronze stripes distinguish these curious fish. In some areas, small groups of lowfin chubs often swim into shallow water to investigate snorklers. It reaches 61 cm (24 in). It eats primarily algae. It occurs in the Indo-Pacific.

redbar hawkfish, *Cirrhitops fasciatus*

bluestripe snapper, *Lutjanus kasmira*

blacktail snapper, *Lutjanus fulvus*

lowfin chub, *Kyphosus vaigiensis*

GOATFISHES

Goatfishes are equipped with highly sensitive barbels under their chins. These barbels are used in probing the bottom for food organisms and are tucked under the chin when not in use. These fish often rest on the bottom on their pelvic fins. Some species form large aggregations. There are seven species commonly seen in Hawaii with a few more that are rare or deep dwelling.

manybar goatfish, *Parupeneus multifasciatus*

These goatfish are recognized by their reddish color and two broad black bars. One bar is under the space between the dorsal fins; another is under the second dorsal fin. A third black spot occurs forward of the tail. A fourth more obscure black area occurs in front of the pectoral fin. This species is normally found swimming in small groups of two or three from inshore to 137 m (450 ft). It reaches 28 cm (11 in). Females mature at 18 cm (7 in), eating foraminifera, crustaceans, snails, octopuses, and fish eggs. This species is found in the South Pacific.

doublebar goatfish, *Parupeneus bifasciatus*

The location of the black bars distinguishes this goatfish from the manybar goatfish. The first bar is located under the front edge of the first dorsal fin, while the other bar occurs under the rear of the second dorsal fin. A third black area may show forward of the tail. It also occurs in large aggregations over sand. It reaches 33 cm (13 in), eating crustaceans, worms, and small fishes mostly at night. Doublebars occur throughout the Indo-Pacific.

manybar goatfish, *Parupeneus multifasciatus*

doublebar goatfish, *Parupeneus bifasciatus*
(photo by John E. Randall)

yellowfin goatfish, *Mulloides vanicolensis*
> The lateral yellow stripe and yellow fins distinguish this species. During the day, yellowfins may be found in large aggregations of several hundred resting on sand bottom or cruising just over it. At night, yellowfin goatfish eat foraminifera, snails, octopuses, crustaceans, and fish eggs. It grows to 38 cm (15 in). It is found throughout the Indo-Pacific.

yellowstripe goatfish, *Mulloides flavolineatus*
> The silver-white body with a lateral yellow stripe broken by a single black spot distinguishes this species. It occurs in large aggregations over sand bottom. This species reaches 40 cm (16 in), eating worms, snails, crabs, shrimps, and fish eggs. It is known throughout the Indo-Pacific.

BUTTERFLYFISHES

Butterflyfishes are an important component of Hawaiian fish populations with at least 22 species known. Worldwide, there are about 144 species. These colorful, disc-shaped reef fishes are unique in several ways. Most have dark, eye bars that conceal the eyes. Butterflyfishes tend to occupy shallow reef areas and most are not usually found below 21 m (70 ft). A few species are known at much greater depths. Butterflyfishes are usually found alone or in pairs, although some species occur in large aggregations. Complex color patterns have evolved largely for species recognition with, perhaps, some role in courtship and mating. Most feed on corals and hydroids, but filamentous algae, zooplankton, and polychaete worms are also eaten. Butterflyfishes' influence on the growth of corals is significant.

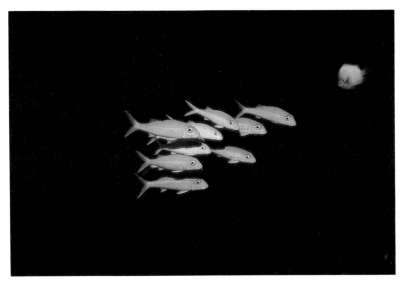

yellowfin goatfish, *Mulloides vanicolensis*

yellowstripe goatfish, *Mulloides flavolineatus*

pyramid butterflyfish, *Hemitaurichthys polylepis*

Unlike most other butterflyfishes, this species is often found in large, scattered aggregations well off the bottom. At Molokini, hundreds of these fish can be found cruising at mid-water to near the surface feeding on zooplankton. It is rarely alone. This species grows to 15 cm (6 in). It is found throughout the central and western Pacific.

reticulated butterflyfish, *Chaetodon reticulatus*

A striking, dark butterflyfish that is uncommon in the Hawaiian Islands, except around Hawaii. It is usually alone or in pairs. It reaches 18 cm (7 in), eating mostly coral polyps and occasionally filamentous algae. It occurs in French Polynesia, the Ryukyus, the Pitcairn group, and the Philippines.

milletseed butterflyfish, *Chaetodon miliaris*

Sometimes called the **lemon butterflyfish**, milletseeds are found in large aggregations at all depths. In some areas, particularly at Molokini, this species aggressively swarms divers looking for handouts. These are the most common butterflyfish in Hawaii. It grows to 16.5 cm (6.5 in), eating mostly zooplankton and occasionally fish parasites (acting as "**cleaners**"). It has a voracious appetite for Hawaiian sergeant and other damselfish eggs. Deep submersibles have found this species at depths of 250 m (820 ft). It occurs only in Hawaii.

blacklip butterflyfish, *Chaetodon kleinii*

The faces of these small butterflyfish are well masked by dark pigment. Blacklip butterflyfishes are common below 18.2 m (60 ft), alone or in pairs. It grows to 11.4 cm (4.5 in), eating zooplankton. It occurs in the Indo-Pacific.

pyramid butterflyfish,
Hemitaurichthys polylepis

reticulated butterflyfish,
Chaetodon reticulatus

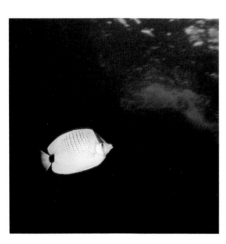

milletseed butterflyfish,
Chaetodon miliaris

blacklip butterflyfish,
Chaetodon kleinii

multiband butterflyfish, *Chaetodon multicinctus*

Multibands appear much more timid than milletseeds and rarely approach divers. It usually occurs in pairs from 5-30 m (16-100 ft) deep. This species reaches 10 cm (4 in), eating primarily coral polyps, but also polychaete worms and small shrimps. It occurs only in Hawaii.

ornate butterflyfish, *Chaetodon ornatissimus*

The white body with diagonal orange lines distinguishes this majestic reef butterflyfish. It is generally found in pairs in areas with moderate surge down to 15 m (50 ft). It grows to 20 cm (8 in), eating primarily coral polyps. This species is found in the central and western Pacific.

teardrop butterflyfish, *Chaetodon unimaculatus*

This timid fish gets its name from the large white-edged black spot that resembles an upsidedown teardrop centered about the mid-lateral line area. It is usually found in pairs or small groups of three or more in areas of prolific coral growth down to 14 m (45 ft). It grows to 18 cm (7 in). Teardrop butterflyfishes eat coral polyps, but will also eat filamentous algae, polychaete worms, and small crustaceans. This species is found in the Indo-Pacific.

multiband butterflyfish, *Chaetodon multicinctus*

ornate butterflyfish, *Chaetodon ornatissimus*

teardrop butterflyfish, *Chaetodon unimaculatus*

bluestripe butterflyfish, *Chaetodon fremblii*
> This species is usually found alone, in pairs or small aggregations in a variety of habitats, but particularly rocky areas down to 61 m (200 ft). It reaches 15 cm (6 in), eating a variety of bottom invertebrates including the tentacles of tubeworms, small crustaceans, and coral polyps. It occurs only in Hawaii.

fourspot butterflyfish, *Chaetodon quadrimaculatus*
> The two white spots on the back distinguishes this species. It is usually in outer reef areas or in shallow water above 10 m (35 ft) where there are boulders, large coral heads, and slight to moderate surge. This species grows to 15 cm (6 in), eating coral polyps. It occurs throughout the South Pacific.

raccoon butterflyfish, *Chaetodon lunula*
> This timid species gets its name from the large black mask that obscures its eyes. It is found alone, in pairs, or mixed in with milletseeds and other fishes in protected areas or exposed reefs. It is active day and night. This species grows to 18 cm (7 in), eating algae, coral polyps, tubeworm tentacles, and nudibranchs. It occurs throughout the Indo-Pacific.

bluestripe butterflyfish, *Chaetodon fremblii*

fourspot butterflyfish, *Chaetodon quadrimaculatus*

raccoon butterflyfish, *Chaetodon lunula*

125

pennantfish, *Heniochus diphreutes*

These unique fish are usually seen in aggregations above the bottom in shallow bays and outer reef areas. Along exposed coasts, pennantfish are generally below 15 m (50 ft) and are known, through submersible observations, to occur down to 183 m (600 ft). This species reaches 20 cm (8 in), eating mainly zooplankton. Pennantfish have been observed acting as "**cleaners**", removing fish parasites. This species occurs from Hawaii and Japan through the Indo-Pacific into the Red Sea.

forcepsfish, *Forcipiger flavissimus*

Often confused with the longnose butterflyfish, which generally lives in deeper water, the forcepsfish is much more abundant and widely distributed throughout the islands. This species is found down to 30 m (100 ft) in areas of heavy coral growth, alone or in small groups. Forcepsfish grow to 18 cm (7 in), eating small crustaceans, the tentacles of tubeworms, the pincers and tubefeet of urchins, and fish eggs. This species is found throughout the Indo-Pacific, the Red Sea, the east coast of Africa, and lower California.

OTHER FISHES

Potter's angelfish, *Centropyge potteri*

These tiny angelfish are usually found alone or mixed in with other fishes near overhangs, boulder piles or coral rubble piles. Potter's angelfish appear to have a strong attachment to a home range and do not wander about. Spawning takes place at dusk from December through May during the week after a full moon. Males of this genus are known to maintain harems. Sex reversal, changing from female to male, has also been discovered in this genus. This angelfish reaches 13 cm (5 in), eating filamentous algae and detritus. It occurs only in Hawaii.

pennantfish, *Heniochus diphreutes*

forcepsfish, *Forcipiger flavissimus*

Potter's angelfish, *Centropyge potteri*

127

bandit angelfish, *Holacanthus arcuatus*

These large angelfish are usually found alone or in pairs below 12 m (40 ft) and are known as deep as 131 m (430 ft). Bandit angelfish grow to 18 cm (7 in), eating algae, sponges, hydroids, and eggs. It occurs only in Hawaii.

DAMSELFISHES

Damselfishes are small, abundant, pugnacious, territorial reef fishes. There are 14 species in the Islands. Some feed on zooplankton, while others have a varied diet. A few species form large aggregations, but most are solitary and live close to the bottom. Eggs are laid on substrate and guarded by aggressive males.

Pacific gregory, *Stegastes fasciolatus*

This dark gray-brown damselfish usually has darker blotches on the sides of the body. Pacific gregorys are one of the more common shallow-water, inshore reef fishes in Hawaii. Gregorys are usually found alone and aggressively defend their territorial home and algae patch against much larger fish. This species grows to 13 cm (5 in), eating algae and detritus. It is found throughout the Indo-Pacific.

Hawaiian dascyllus, *Dascyllus albisella*

These are among Hawaii's most striking damselfishes. These pugnacious damselfish often swim in a roller coaster fashion around their territorial coral heads. During the day, these fish are usually found in small groups hovering over or darting in and out of the branches of antler coral, *Pocillopora eydouxi* or cauliflower coral, *P. meandrina*. At night the color is nearly all black, except for a single white spot. Occasionally, these fish are found in large aggregations feeding on zooplankton as much as 6 m (20 ft) above the bottom. This species grows to 13 cm (5 in). It occurs only in Hawaii.

bandit angelfish, *Holacanthus arcuatus*

Pacific gregory, *Stegastes fasciolatus*

Hawaiian dascyllus,
Dascyllus albisella (in daylight)

Hawaiian dascyllus,
(at night)

chocolate-dip chromis, *Chromis hanui*

These dark brown damselfish with pure white tails are easily recognized among all the other bottom fish. This chromis is usually alone or in small groups from shallow areas to 50.3 m (165 ft). It reaches 9 cm (3.5 in), eating mainly zooplankton. This species occurs only in Hawaii.

threespot chromis, *Chromis verator*

Threespots are dark-gray to blackish damselfish with three small, sometimes faint, white spots at the rear of the body. These are deep water fishes rarely found in less than 18 m (60 ft), but as deep as 182 m (600 ft). This is the third largest damselfish in Hawaiian waters, reaching 22 cm (8.5 in). Threespot chromis eats zooplankton, particularly copepods. Like some other damselfishes, this species occurs only in Hawaii.

agile chromis, *Chromis agilis*

These damselfish are distinguished by the pink to lavender coloration around the head and chest, and the black spot at the base of the pectoral fins. These fish are found from 4.6 to 61 m (15 to 200 ft) deep. This species appears to be more abundant on the lee sides of islands. It reaches 11 cm (4.4 in) and occurs throughout the Indo-Pacific.

Hawaiian sergeant, *Abudefduf abdominalis*

This is Hawaii's largest and most aggressive damselfish. From December through July, pugnacious males persistently guard nests of red-purple eggs on the sides of rocks. Males chase other fishes away, including larger species. If a male is drawn away from the nest by an aggressive intruder, wrasses, butterflyfishes, and others quickly dart in to eat the eggs. Hawaiian sergeants grow to 25 cm (10 in). Sometimes these fish will rise off the bottom to feed on plankton. Algae is also eaten. This species is found only in Hawaii.

chocolate-dip chromis,
Chromis hanui

threespot chromis, *Chromis verato*

agile chromis, *Chromis agilis*

Hawaiian sergeant,
Abudefduf abdominalis

WRASSES

Wrasses comprise the largest family of fish in Hawaii with 42 species known. Wrasses generally have pronounced teeth used to crush urchins, crabs, or coral. Sex reversal is known among several species. Individuals begin adult life as females and later change to more brightly colored males. This phase is referred to as the "**terminal phase**" and the males as "**terminal males**". Color patterns are bright, complex, and different for sexes. Many wrasses respond to decreasing light levels at dusk by burying themselves in sand. Following sunrise, wrasses are among the last fishes on the reef to awake and proceed with the business of daily life.

Hawaiian cleaner wrasse, *Labroides phthirophagus*
Juveniles are black with bright blue lines. Cleaner wrasses are important to the health of most reef fishes. This wrasse specializes in picking parasites off the bodies of other fishes while incidentally feeding on mucus and scales. Unlike other species that must search for food, cleaner wrasses wait for infected fish to seek their services. This species is found alone or in pairs in defined territories that serve as their **cleaning stations**. Hawaiian cleaner wrasses swim up and down in a rollercoaster fashion, back and forth around their stations advertising their services. Other fishes signal their interest in cleaning services by tilting their bodies sideways, or head down-tail up, or head up-tail down. Cleaner wrasses occur down to 91 m (300 ft). This wrasse grows to 10 cm (4 in). Unlike most other wrasses, cleaner wrasses do not bury themselves in the sand at night, but wrap themselves in a mucus blanket like many parrotfish. This species occurs only in Hawaii.

Hawaiian cleaner wrasse, *Labroides phthirophagus*
(adult)

Hawaiian cleaner wrasse, *Labroides phthirophagus*
(juvenile)

saddle wrasse, *Thalassoma duperrey*

Saddle wrasses are among the most curious and aggressive fish on the reef. Their habit of following divers and snorkelers looking for food often leads to lightly nipped fingers. This species is also the most abundant inshore fish in Hawaii, commonly found in small aggregations; rarely alone. It occurs down to 21 m (70 ft) and grows to 25 cm (10 in). Saddle wrasses eat worms, brittle stars, urchins, and small crustaceans. Juveniles and some adults have been observed removing parasites from other fishes. This wrasse occurs only in Hawaii.

blacktail wrasse, *Thalassoma ballieui*

Blacktails differ from other Hawaiian members of this genus in that the initial color phase of juveniles and adult males is similar. Blacktails are usually found alone, sometimes well off the bottom. This wrasse reaches 38 cm (15 in), eating urchins, brittle stars, sea stars, crabs, lobsters, snails, snail and fish eggs, and fishes. It occurs only in Hawaii.

ornate wrasse, *Halichoeres ornatissimus*

These multi-colored wrasses are usually found alone or in small numbers in inshore areas. Ornate wrasses reach 15 cm (6 in), eating small mollusks and crustaceans. This wrasse occurs throughout the South Pacific.

shortnose wrasse, *Macropharyngodon geoffroy*

These spotted wrasses are usually found alone or in small groups from 6-30 m (20 to 100 ft) deep. This wrasse grows to 5 cm (6 in). It has specialized teeth used to crush the shells of the mollusks and foraminifera it eats. This wrasse occurs only in Hawaii.

saddle wrasse,
Thalassoma duperrey

blacktail wrasse, *Thalassoma ballieui*

ornate wrasse,
Halichoeres ornatissimus

shortnose wrasse,
Macropharyngodon geoffroy

smalltail wrasse, *Pseudojuloides cerasinus*

These small wrasses are usually found in groups, close to rubble or live coral. These wrasses are not usually seen in water less than 18 m (60 ft). Juveniles are cherry-brick red. Females are light red above and white below. Males are olive-green above and light blue below with two lateral stripes of bright blue and yellow. This species reaches 12 cm (5 in). It occurs in the Indo-Pacific.

yellowtail coris, *Coris gaimard*

One of Hawaii's most extravagantly colored fishes, the yellowtail coris is usually found alone. While adults have patterns of bright blue, yellow, rose, and green, juveniles are bright red-orange with three black-edged white spots along the sides. Adults reach 38 cm (15 in), and eat small urchins, brittle stars, shrimps and other invertebrates. This species is found in the Indo-Pacific.

ringtail wrasse, *Cheilinus unifasciatus*

These fishes are distinguished by the ringed tails and the orange bars radiating from the eyes and across the cheeks. These large wrasses are often seen cruising alone well off the bottom. It has been found from 9-160 m (30-528 ft) deep. Adults reach 46 cm (18 in), eating crabs, brittle stars, urchins, and fishes. This species is found throughout the tropical Pacific.

Hawaiian hogfish, *Bodianus bilunulatus*

Females are light yellow, striped, and with a large black spot under the rear section of the soft dorsal rays. Males are wine-purple. Hogfish are normally seen cruising alone off the bottom. It occurs from 8-110 m (25 to 360 ft). Adults grow to 51 cm (20 in), eating urchins, brittle stars, crustaceans, mollusks, and occasionally small fishes. This species occurs in the South Pacific, the western Pacific, and the Indian Ocean.

smalltail wrasse, *Pseudojuloides cerasinus*

yellowtail coris, *Coris gaimard*

ringtail wrasse,
Cheilinus unifasciatus

Hawaiian hogfish, *Bodianus bilunulatus*

PARROTFISHES

Parrotfishes are large, brightly colored reef fishes with plate-like teeth used in scraping thin layers of algae or chipping off pieces of coral. Parrotfishes are efficient herbivores, scraping and grinding large quantities of coral rubble to get algae. As a result, parrotfishes produce vast amounts of sand. Sexes are dramatically different in color. Sex reversal occurs with **terminal males** assuming bright blue or green colors. Individuals sleep on the bottom at night. Some enclose themselves in a net or veil-like cocoon of mucus. The males of some species have sexual territories and mate with one female at a time. Group spawning occurs in other species.

stareye parrotfish, *Calotomus carolinus*

> Stareyes sleep without a mucus veil. A terminal male is shown here. The orange-pink bars radiating from the eyes are distinctive. Stareyes are usually seen alone cruising or grazing on the reef. Adults grow to 50 cm (20 in). This parrotfish is found in the Indo-Pacific and tropical eastern Pacific.

bullethead parrotfish, *Scarus sordidus*

> Terminal males are distinguished by the large, lateral pale orange or yellow areas. Females and juveniles are gray to dark brown with reddish lips and chins. This is one of the most abundant parrotfishes in its range. Adults grow to 38 cm (15 in). The young are often seen mixed in with large aggregations of convict tangs during their feeding forays. This species occurs throughout the Indo-Pacific.

stareye parrotfish, *Calotomus carolinus*

bullethead parrotfish, *Scarus sordidus*

OTHER FISH

Moorish idol, *Zanclus cornutus*
> As suggested by its unique body design, the Moorish idol is in a family by itself. The third dorsal spine is filamentous and may be extremely long in older animals. While its tubular mouth is ideal for reaching into tight crevices, it is more often seen feeding on easily accessible sponge encrusted rock surfaces. Moorish idols are frequently found alone or in small groups in caves or under ledges picking at sponges, algae, and other items. Adults reach 20 cm (8 in) in length. These fishes have been found as deep as 183 m (600 ft). Moorish idols occur throughout the Indo-Pacific and tropical eastern Pacific.

SURGEONFISHES

Surgeonfishes or tangs are easily recognized by one or two razor-sharp spines located on each side of the caudal peduncle. These spines are used in defense. Tangs will often back up to an intruding fish to threaten laceration by flagging the tail. The threat is usually enough to discourage them. Some species use their pectoral fins for forward movement, while others use their tails to propel them.

achilles tang, *Acanthurus achilles*
> These aggressive, chocolate tangs seem to prefer moderately turbulent areas where waves wash over or against rocks and walls. Occurring alone or in small groups, achilles tangs have little tolerance for other surgeonfishes. Adults grow to 5 cm (10 in), grazing on filamentous and leafy algae. This species occurs in several island chains of the South Pacific.

Moorish idol, *Zanclus cornutu*

achilles tang, *Acanthurus achilles*

convict tang, *Acanthurus triostegus*

These tangs or **"manini"** are among the more eye-catching and the most abundant tangs in the islands. Convicts occur in a variety of habitats from shore to about 45 m (150 ft). Unlike other tangs, young convicts are frequently seen close inshore. Adults reach 25 cm (10 in), eating mostly filamentous algae. These tangs move across coral rubble areas in large, fairly close-knit aggregations of 200 or more grazing fish. Their intense feeding behavior often attracts other fishes who swim or feed with them. Spawning occurs from December through July, when large numbers assemble near dusk. From these aggregations, small groups of males and females dart upward about 2.4 m (8 ft), releasing eggs and sperm into the sea. Convict tangs occur throughout the Indo-Pacific and tropical eastern Pacific.

orangeband surgeonfish, *Acanthurus olivaceus*

This species is usually gray-brown with the horizontal orange band. Some individuals are paler in the front half of the body than the back half. Orangeband surgeonfish are often seen swimming alone or in small groups over sandy bottom near reefs. This species is usually found from 9-45 m (30 to 150 ft). Adults reach 30 cm (12 in), eating diatoms, filamentous algae and detritus. These tangs occur in the central and western Pacific.

eye-stripe surgeonfish, *Acanthurus dussumieri*

Known to Hawaiians as **"palani"**, the eye-stripe surgeonfish is a large, regal-looking fish that cruises alone or with other fishes over sand bottom, coral rubble, or rocky areas. Individuals rarely venture into water less than 9 m (30 ft) deep. Adults grow to 46 cm (18 in), eating diatoms, green and blue-green algae, and detritus. This species occurs primarily in the Hawaiian and Line Islands.

convict tang, *Acanthurus triostegus*

orangeband surgeonfish, *Acanthurus olivaceus*

eye-stripe surgeonfish, *Acanthurus dussumieri*

goldring surgeonfish, *Ctenochaetus strigosus*

Goldring surgeonfish, or "**kole tangs**", are usually found mixed in with other species including non-surgeons. Their distinctive yellow eye ring separates them from all other brown surgeonfishes. This species occurs from shallow inshore areas to over 46 m (150 ft). Adults reach 18 cm (7 in), eating detritus with their comb-like teeth. Goldring surgeonfish are abundant in Hawaii; rare in the Indo-Pacific.

yellow tang, *Zebrasoma flavescens*

Like so many tropical or semi-tropical species, yellow tangs are brilliantly colored. Yellow tangs are usually found in small groups; although when spawning occurs, large numbers assemble. This species occurs from calm shallow water to over 46 m (150 ft). This tang appears to be more abundant on the lee sides of islands. Adults reach 20 cm (8 in), eating filamentous algae. Yellow tangs are found in several island groups including the Marshalls, the Marianas, Wake Island, and off southern Japan.

bluespine unicornfish, *Naso unicornis*

As their name suggests, these surgeonfish are distinguished by the bright blue spines and surrounding areas. This surgeonfish often cruises alone or in small groups over shallow areas of the reef. It is one of the largest surgeonfishes in Hawaii, reaching 69 cm (27 in). These fish eat leafy, brown algae like *Sargassum sp.* and *Dictyota sp.*. It occurs throughout the Indo-Pacific.

goldring surgeonfish, *Ctenochaetus strigos*

yellow tang, *Zebrasoma flavescens*

bluespine unicornfish, *Naso unicornis*

sleek unicornfish, *Naso hexacanthus*

The body color varies from dark brown to pale blue. Sleek unicornfish are usually found along reef edges where there are strong currents. These surgeonfish are rarely found in shallow water of less than 5.2 m (50 ft) and are known at depths of 137 m (450 ft). Sleek unicornfish reach 76 cm (30 in), eating zooplankton. It occurs in the Indo-Pacific.

orangespine unicornfish, *Naso lituratus*

These surgeonfish are basically gray with bright orange around the spines. This species is usually found alone or in small groups offshore. Large, older males have long filaments extending from the lobes of the tail. Adults grow to 46 cm (18 in), eating leafy brown algae like *Sargassum sp.* and *Dictyota sp.*. It occurs throughout the Indo-Pacific.

OTHER FISHES

Ewa blenny, *Plagiotremus ewaensis*

These blennies are recognized by the orange-yellow body and black-edged blue lateral stripes. Ewa blennies have large canine teeth in the lower jaw that fit into sockets in the roof of the mouth and are used for defense. Ewa blennies are found from 9-55 m (30-180 ft). It uses worm or snail shells for shelter. Adults grow to 10 cm (4 in), feeding on the skin, scales, and mucus of other fishes. Individuals hover over the bottom waiting for an unsuspecting fish to come within range of their quick attack. This fish will also nip divers occasionally, but the bite is hardly noticeable. It occurs only in Hawaii.

sleek unicornfish, *Naso hexacanthus*

orangespine unicornfish, *Naso lituratus*

Ewa blenny, *Plagiotremus ewaensis*

barred filefish, *Cantherhines dumerilii*

Filefish superficially resemble triggers, but belong in their own family. The gray-brown, light-olive body of this species has 12 faint brown bars towards the orange tail. Adults grow to 35 cm (14 in), eating mostly branching corals and some urchins, sea stars, and bryozoans. This fish occurs from East Africa to the tropical eastern Pacific.

fantail filefish, *Pervagor spilosoma*

These fish are recognized by the yellow background with many small black spots and an erect first dorsal spine. These fish can be found alone near the bottom or cruising in large aggregations in mid-water. Fantail filefish are common from shallow, inshore areas to over 46 m (150 ft). This filefish grows to 18 cm (7 in), eating algae, detritus, foraminifera, sponges, mollusks, crustaceans, urchins, and tunicates. It occurs only in Hawaii.

barred filefish, *Cantherhines dumerilii*

fantail filefish, *Pervagor spilosoma*

TRIGGERFISHES

Triggerfish get their name from the second dorsal spine which acts like a trigger by locking the first spine in position, creating a defensive weapon. There are ten species in Hawaii. These fishes are active in daylight. When darkness or danger approaches, triggerfishes seek the shelter of holes in the reef where they wedge themselves in. Observations suggest that each has a preferred hole. Triggerfish swim primarily through undulating movements of the second dorsal and anal fins.

pinktail durgon, *Melichthys vidua*

> Pinktail durgons are usually seen alone or with other species when feeding or cleaning is occurring. Some occur as deep as 140 m (460 ft). Adults grow to 33 cm (13 in), eating mostly algae and detritus. This durgon also takes sponges, crabs, octopuses, and small fishes. It occurs in the Indo-Pacific.

black durgon, *Melichthys niger*

> Black durgons are wary fish commonly seen in large, scattered aggregations swimming well off the bottom or near the surface, particularly when there is a boat nearby. Adults grow to 33 cm (13 in), eating attached or drifting algae and zooplankton. Black durgons have a circumtropical distribution under a variety of synonyms.

lei triggerfish, *Sufflamen bursa*

> These approachable, light gray triggerfishes are normally found alone near the bottom. Lei triggerfish have two dark brown or mustard-yellow, crescent-shaped, vertical bars between the pectoral fin and the back of the eye. This species ranges from 3-91 m (10-300 ft). Lei triggers grow to 21.5 cm (8.5 in), eating algae, detritus, worms, mollusks, crustaceans, tunicates, and fish eggs. It occurs in the Indo-Pacific.

pinktail durgon, *Melichthys vidua*

black durgon, *Melichthys niger*
(photo by Ed Robinson)

lei triggerfish, *Sufflamen bursa*

spotted trunkfish, *Ostracion meleagris*
Trunkfish are often called "**boxfish**" for their somewhat quadrangular body design. The Hawaiian population of this species is colored differently than populations elsewhere. These trunkfish are usually seen alone near rocks or coral heads and are the most common trunkfish in Hawaii. These fish can release a toxic skin substance under stress that may ward off enemies. Adults reach 5 cm (6 in), eating algae, sponges, and tunicates. This species occurs in the Indo-Pacific and tropical eastern Pacific.

Hawaiian whitespotted toby, *Canthigaster jactator*
These small, blimp-like puffers are abundant in shallow, inshore areas near the bases of coral heads, alone or in pairs. These fish are rarely far from the shelter of coral. Puffers get their name from their ability to inflate themselves with water in self-defense. Because the fins of this species are transparent, body movement is difficult to detect as these fish swim. This feature may help them sneak up on some prey. Adults reach 9 cm (3.5 in), eating algae, detritus, sponges, zoanthids, worms, bryozoans, crustaceans, urchins, brittle stars, tunicates, and fishes. This species occurs only in Hawaii.

stripebelly puffer, *Arothron hispidus*
These giant puffers are found in a variety of habitats including estuaries and inshore sand flats. At night, stripebelly puffers often sleep out in the open on sand bottom. During the day, these puffers are frequently seen cruising over sand. Adults reach 48 cm (19 in), eating algae, coral, zoanthids, hydroids, sponges, worms, mollusks, crustaceans, and echinoderms. This species occurs in the Indo-Pacific and tropical eastern Pacific.

spotted trunkfish, *Ostracion meleagris*

Hawaiian whitespotted toby, *Canthigaster jactator*

stripebelly puffer, *Arothron hispidus*

green sea turtle, *Chelonia mydas*

Green turtles are **protected** by federal law from being disturbed or even touched. Turtles are occasionally found swimming over the reef or resting on underwater ledges. Full-grown adults may reach 300 pounds. Each spring, adult males and some females migrate to French Frigate Shoals, in the Northwestern Hawaiian Islands, to breed. Eggs are laid in sand along stretches of beach rarely visited by people. Many young hatchlings are eaten by ghost crabs and seabirds before they reach the relative safety of the sea. In the sea, green turtles occasionally fall prey to tiger sharks. Turtles eat mainly algae. **HELP**: If you see this turtle while snorkeling or diving, please enjoy it from a distance. This turtle has a wide range throughout the Indo-Pacific.

green sea turtle, *Chelonia mydas*

CORAL REEF ETIQUETTE

WHAT YOU CAN DO

WHILE DIVING:

1. If you use your own boat, anchor it in sand bottom only.

2. Before jumping into the water, check the depth clearance. Avoid "**giant stride**" entries in shallow reef areas to protect yourself and delicate branching corals.

3. Use just enough weights to achieve neutral buoyancy and continuously adjust your B.C. to avoid crashing into the bottom on descent or while swimming over the reef.

4. Stay far enough above the bottom while exploring to avoid fin contact with coral or kicking up sediment.

5. Clip your gauges and other loose gear to your B.C. to prevent them from dragging across delicate corals and other marine life.

6. Avoid touching live coral; a simple touch can kill polyps. Look for algae-covered coral rubble or rocks to steady yourself.

7. If you roll coral rubble or rocks looking for invertebrates, replace them exactly as you found them. Most of the animals living beneath or attached to the bottom of rocks are not adapted to bright light, currents, and sedimentation.

8. When in caves or tight spaces, avoid banging into walls or ceilings with your tank or fins.

9.   Avoid kicking up sand. It smothers delicate invertebrates like corals, sponges, and tunicates.

10.   Avoid feeding fishes. Artificial foods can be unhealthy to fish and promote aggressiveness. It's better to leave them to their natural diets.

11.   In strong currents, look for algae-covered coral rubble and clean rock to pull yourself along or to hold on to.

12.   Leave live animals and plants in the water.

13.   Removing attached animals or plants for photographic posing will stress or kill them.

14.   Do not stay long in caves or in any one spot in caves. Large amounts of trapped air in ceiling pockets kills the animals attached there.

15.   Make sure your weightbelt is secure. A free-falling weightbelt crushes immobile plants and animals, and divers below you.

WHILE SNORKELING OR TIDEPOOLING:

1.   Replace all rocks, boulders, and coral rubble exactly where and how you found them. Creatures permanently attached and sensitive to light and drying out will perish, if you don't.

2.   Avoid all contact with live coral.

3.   Leave "apparently" empty shells in the water. They often have hermit crabs hiding deep within.

4.   Look before placing your feet down when walking in shallow water.

5.   Throwing rocks into the water can break and kill delicate coral branches.

6.   Save your lunch, film, and other litter for proper disposal.

PRETEND you are walking through an art gallery filled with the world's finest and most precious paintings, sculptures, tapestries, and embroidery as you explore Hawaiian reefs, and act accordingly.

GLOSSARY

Acontia: Special threads bearing nematocysts or stinging cells that are expelled from the bodies of some anemones in response to irritation or disturbance and as a defensive action.

Ambulacral Groove: The furrow running from the underside of the tip of the arm to the mouth in sea stars.

Aristotle's Lantern: The calcareous plates shaped like an old lantern that creates the mouth of a sea urchin.

Carapace: The outer bony or calcium carbonate shell of certain animals like turtles and crabs. Also applied to the outer armor-like covering of trunkfishes.

Caudal Peduncle: That narrow portion of a fish's body just forward of the tail fin.

Cuvierian Tubules: The spaghetti-like internal organs of sea cucumbers that are disgorged when they are disturbed.

Foraminifera: A group of single-celled protozoan animals with calcareous shells.

Indo-Pacific: The bio-geographic region encompassing the tropical Indian Ocean and the central and western Pacific Oceans.

Invertebrates: Refers to animals without backbones including worms, nudibranchs, crabs, corals and the like.

Lateral Line: A visible line running along the sides of fish's bodies that indicates an underlying, fluid-filled, sensory canal that functions in perception of low-frequency vibrations.

Melanesia: A group of islands in the southwestern Pacific including: Vanuatu, Santa Cruz, Fiji, Solomons, New Caledonia, and the Admiralty Islands.

Micronesia: A group of islands in the southwestern Pacific including: Wake, Marshalls, Marianas, Palau, Carolines, Kribati, Johnston Islands.

Mucus Ropes: A viscous material produced by coral animals in response to exposure during extreme low tide as a possible defense against desiccation.

Nocturnal: An animal that is primarily active at night.

Oceania: The islands of the Pacific including: Melanesia, Micronesia, Polynesia, and sometimes New Zealand, Australia, and the Malay Archipelago.

Operculum: The gill cover of fishes or horny plate that closes opening to snail shells.

Polynesia: A group of islands in the South Pacific including: Tahiti, Marquesas, Pitcairn, Australs, Tuamotus, Phoenix, Tuvalu, Samoa, Tonga, Cooks, and Line Islands.

Photosynthesis: A process in which chlorophyll-bearing plants utilize carbon dioxide and water in the presence of sunlight to produce some of their own food (carbohydrates) with oxygen as a by-product.

Plankton: Refers to microscopic plants and animals that are suspended in water and serve as the base of the marine food chain. The larval forms of many animals like crabs are planktonic.

Polyps: Individual coral or hydroid animals with oral rings of stinging tentacles, often living together as colonies.

Portunid: Swimming crabs recognized by the flattened, paddle-like fifth pair of legs.

Seamounts: Submerged undersea mountains.

Symbiosis: A relationship between two animals where at least one animal is dependent on the other or where they both mutually benefit from their association.

Vertebrates: Refers to animals with backbones including fishes, reptiles, amphibians, birds and mammals.

Zooplankton: The animal members of the plankton community.

Zooxanthellae: Unicellular, dinoflagellate algae that usually live inside the tissues of anemones, corals, and some nudibranchs.

REFERENCES

Allen, Gerald R. **Damselfishes of the South Seas**. New Jersey: T.F.H. Publications; 1975

Allen, Gerald R. **Butterfly and Angelfishes of the World V2**. New York: John Wiley and Sons; 1979

Allen, Gerald R. and Roger C. Steene. **Reef Fishes of the Indian Ocean**. New Jersey: T.F.H. Publications; 1987

Bagnis, Raymond. **Underwater Guide to Tahiti.** Tahiti: Les Editions du Pacifique; 1980

Barnes, Robert D. **Invertebrate Zoology**. Philadelphia: Saunders College/Holt, Rinehart, and Winston; 1980

Bertsch, H. and S. Johnson. **Hawaiian Nudibranchs**. Honolulu: The Oriental Publishing Co.; 1981

Coleman, Neville. **Encyclopedia of Marine Animals**. Australia: Collins, Angus & Robertson Publishers, Ltd.; 1991

Devaney, Dennis M. and Lucius G. Eldredge Editors. **Reef and Shore Fauna of Hawaii Section 1**. Honolulu: Bernice P. Bishop Museum Special Publication 64(1). Bishop Museum Press; 1977

Fielding, Ann. **Hawaiian Reefs and Tidepools**. Honolulu: The Oriental Publishing Co.; 1979

Fielding, Ann and Ed Robinson. **An Underwater Guide To Hawaii**. Honolulu: Univ. of Hawaii Press; 1990

Gosline, William A. **Structure, Function, and Ecology in the Goatfishes (Family Mulidae).** Pacific Science 38(4); 1984

Gosliner, Terrence M. **The Systematics of the Aeolidacea (Nudibranchia:Mollusca) of the Hawaiian Islands, with Description of Two New Species.** Pacific Science 33(1); 1979

Hobson, Edmund S. **Feeding Relationships of Teleostean Fishes on Coral Reefs in Kona Hawaii.** Fishery Bulletin. 74(4); 1974

Hobson, Edmund and E.H.Chave. **Hawaiian Reef Animals.** Honolulu: Univ. of Hawaii Press; 1990

Holthus, Paul F. and James E. Maragos and Christopher W. Evans. **Coral Reef Recovery Subsequent to the Freshwater Kill of 1965 in Kaneohe Bay, Oahu, Hawaii.** Pacific Science 43(2); 1989

Kay, E. Allison and David K. Young. **Hawaiian Doridacea (Opisthobranchia:Mollusca).** Pacific Science 23(2); 1969

Kay, E. Allison. **Hawaiian Marine Shells, Reef and Shore Fauna of Hawaii Section 4.** Honolulu: Bernice P. Bishop Museum Special Publication 64(4). Bishop Museum Press; 1979

Kay, E. Allison and Olive Schoenberg-Dole. **Shells of Hawaii.** Honolulu: Univ. of Hawaii Press; 1991

Kropp, Roy K. **Revision of the Genera of Gall Crabs (Crustacea:Cryptochiridae) Occuring in the Pacific Ocean.** Pacific Science 44(4); 1990

Krupp, David A. **Mucus Production by Corals Exposed During an Extreme Low Tide**. Pacific Science 38(1); 1984

Magruder, W.H. and J. Hunt. **Seaweeds of Hawaii**. Honolulu: The Oriental Publishing Co.; 1979

Myers, Robert F. **Micronesian Reef Fishes**. Territory of Guam: Coral Graphics; 1991

Newbert, Christopher. **Within a Rainbowed Sea**. Oregon: Beyond Words Publishing; 1990

Pawlik, Joseph R. **The Spanish Dancer Nudibranch**. Oceanus 35(1); 1992

Randall, John E. **New Records of Fishes from the Hawaiian Islands**. Pacific Science 34(3); 1980

Randall, John E. **Guide To Hawaiian Reef Fishes**. Pennsylvania: Harrowood Books; 1985

Schroeder, Robert E. **Philippine Shore Fishes of the Western Sulu Sea**. Philippines: Bureau of Fisheries and Aquatic Resources and National Media Production Center Books; 1980

Severns, Mike and Pauline Fiene. **Molokini Island - Hawaii's Premier Marine Reserve**. Hawaii: Pacific Islands Publishing, Ltd.; 1993

Steene, Roger C. **Butterfly and Angelfishes of the World V1**. New York: John Wiley and Sons; 1977

Steene, Roger C. **Coral Reefs - Nature's Richest Realm**. New York: Mallard Press; 1990

Stoddart, D.R. **Biogeography of The Tropical Pacific.** Pacific Science 46(2); 1992

Tinker, Spencer Wilkie. **Fishes of Hawaii**. Honolulu: Hawaiian Services Inc.; 1978

Veron, J. E. N. **Corals of Australia and The Indo-Pacific.** Honolulu; University of Hawaii Press; 1993

Walker, George P.L. **Geology and Volcanology of the Hawaiian Islands.** Pacific Science 44(4); 1990

White, Alan. **Philippine Coral Reefs**. Philippines: New Day Publishers; 1987

Wood, Elizabeth M. **Corals of The World.** New Jersey: T.F.H. Publications, Inc.; 1983

ABSTRACTS

Information from the following abstracts were taken from the Albert L. Tester Memorial Symposia published in Pacific Science, University of Hawaii Press.

Baer, Lawrence J. **Agonistic Communication and Dominance in Hawaiian Yellow Tangs,** *Zebrasoma flavescens* **(Acanthuridae).** Pacific Science 33(1); 1979

Cox, Evelyn. **The Effects of Selective Predation on Growth and Competitive Interactions between Two Corals,** *Montipora verrucosa* and *Porites compressa,* **in Kaneohe Bay, Oahu.** Pacific Science 38(4); 1984

Fitzhardinge, Rachel. **Some Preliminary Observations on Coral Recruitment in Kaneohe Bay, Oahu.** Pacific Science 38(4); 1984

Fitzhardinge, Rachel. **The Effects of Fish Grazing on Juvenile Corals.** Pacific Science 39(4); 1985

Gallien, Wm. Brad. **A Comparison of Hydrodynamic Forces on Two Sympatric Sea Urchins: Implications of Morphology and Habitat.** Pacific Science 40(1-4); 1986

Hourigan, Thomas F. **The Distribution and Abundance of Coral-Feeding Butterflyfishes at Puako, Hawaii.** Pacific Science 38(1); 1984

Hourigan, Thomas F. **Pair Bond Formation in Two Species of Hawaiian Butterflyfishes (Chaetodontidae).** Pacific Science 38(4); 1984

Walsh, William J. **Responses of a Hawaiian Reef Fish Community to a Catastrophic Storm.** Pacific Science 34(3); 1980

INDEX

ABOUT WAVECREST PUBLICATIONS

Wavecrest Publications was created to produce a series of books focusing on the intricate balance and unusual behavior of marine life from reefs around the world. Because of a deep commitment to the conservation and non-consumptive enjoyment of reefs and reef creatures, the Author consciously omits information on the cultural use of marine life. While we acknowledge the crucial dependence of people on marine resources for food, medicine, and minerals, the Author and Publisher do not want to encourage the removal of any species by visitors to these islands for food, decor, or sale. Wherever possible, we stress behavior that allows observation and enjoyment by divers and snorkelers without damaging the resources.

The oceans of the world have been the dumping grounds for industrial, military, and human wastes, while also being overharvested by "quick-profit" minded companies and individuals.

The marine treasures found along coastal areas within the depths accessible to most sport divers are ours not to squander, but to conserve for our children and theirs.

Join us in fostering greater interest and action in preserving healthy, biologically-rich marine environments.

FUTURE BOOKS IN THIS SERIES:
   Caribbean Reefs
   California Reefs
   Red Sea Reefs

ABOUT THE AUTHOR

Ron has been diving in Hawaiian waters since 1979 and has spent several hundred hours underwater. His diving interests began when he fell out of a raft at Fitzgerald Marine Reserve in California in 1956 and landed near a sunstar. Awed by that

chance encounter, he purchased a sheet of neoprene rubber and made his first wet suit in order to get a closer look at all those wonderful creatures. Since then, he has been diving in a variety of places including Hawaii, the Caribbean, French Polynesia, as well as the California Coast. Much of Ron's background and interests center around the sea.

He has written several dozen articles on various marine life including Hawaiian fish in **Oceans**, **Pacific Discovery**, and **Sea Frontiers**. He also authored field guides including: **Pacific Intertidal Life, Pacific Coast Fish**, **Pacific Coast Mammals**, and **Mountain State Mammals**. He has been a naturalist with the East Bay Regional Park District in California for over 28 years, where he is currently Chief Naturalist. In 1989, Ron received the distinguished Fellow Award from the National Association for Interpretation, the professional organization for naturalists in the United States.